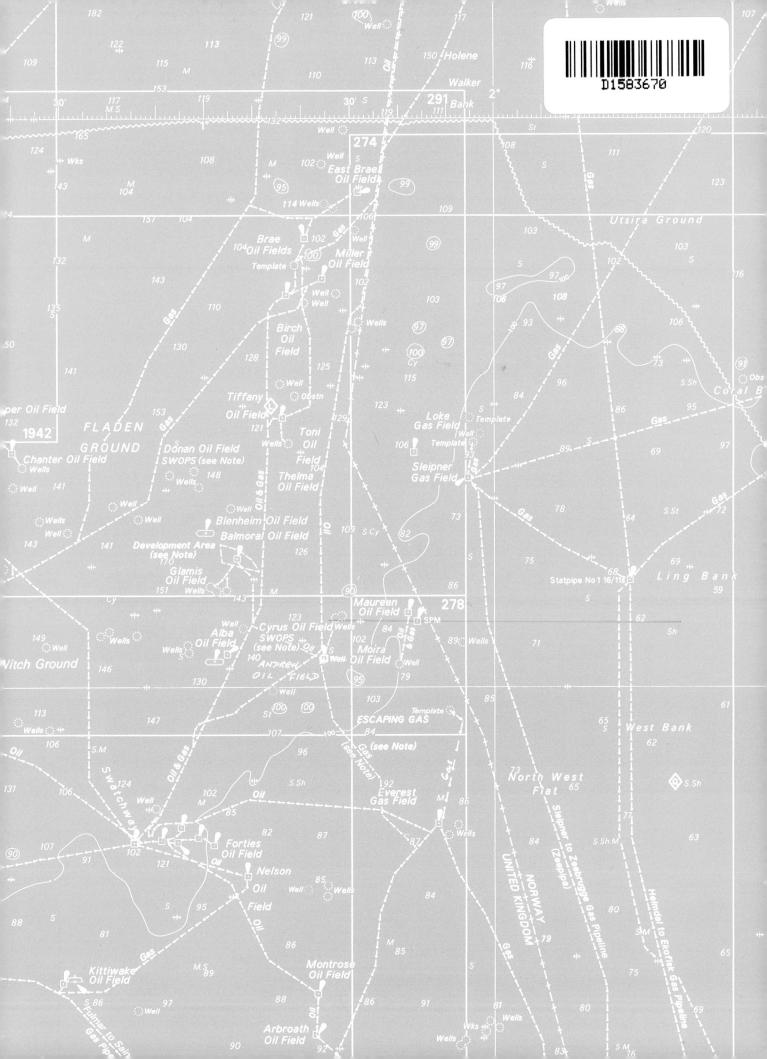

No business as usual

An extraordinary North Sea result

Terry Knott

Acknowledgements

The author would like to thank BP, its partners, and the Andrew facilities alliance for the opportunity to research and write this book. Thanks are expressed in particular to John Martin and Paul Bibby for making this work possible and for their support throughout the project. The early assistance of Ash Bakshi and Barry Smale is gratefully acknowledged, as are the contributions of the alliance project managers for providing invaluable insight into the co-operative efforts of the Andrew team.

Special thanks go to Norman Brown for his help in organising the gathering of information from a rich variety of sources, and to Bill Ebdon, Brian Gebruers, John Jerzak and Yaniv Melitz for their input and practical support during production. The author is also indebted to Valerie Shepard for generously volunteering time and much valued publishing advice, as well as to the staff of BP's Photographic Library and the team at Thumb Design.

The many people who contributed their first-hand knowledge of the Andrew development are too numerous to name individually, but their input created the fabric of this book, in detail and in spirit. The author expresses his thanks to each of them.

A final note of gratitude is due to family and friends, whose understanding and encouragement have been so readily forthcoming.

No business as usual
Copyright © 1996 Terry Knott All rights reserved

Published in 1996 by The British Petroleum Company p.l.c.
Britannic House 1 Finsbury Circus London EC2M 7BA United Kingdom

ISBN 0 86165 202 9

Designed and produced by Thumb Design using RingMaster®

Printed and bound in England by Litho-Tech

Photographic acknowledgements
Leif Anund Norman Edwards David Evans Flying Focus David Gold DGS Films Brian Kiloh
Barry Lewis/Network Northern Counties Nicki Sakelaropoulus BP Photographic Library
Brown & Root Photographic Library Members of the Andrew and Cyrus project teams
Suppliers to the projects The author

Cover photograph: Tony Stone Images

Crown copyright material reproduced on inside covers/endpapers from Admiralty chart 2182C by permission of the Controller of HMSO and the hydrographic offices of Norway and the United Kingdom

While every care has been taken to ensure that the information contained in this book is correct, the author and publisher accept no liability for decisions made on the basis of information contained herein

Contents

Cost figures included in this book are recorded where possible as fourth quarter 1993 monetary values for comparison with the Andrew facilities sanctioned cost

Foreword

No business as usual relates the story of an oilfield development with a difference. From a portfolio of unpromising prospects in the North Sea, the Andrew field was selected by British Petroleum to serve in the vanguard of the company's drive toward improving both business performance and the long term outlook for the offshore oil industry. From doubtful beginnings, the Andrew story becomes one which embraces the intertwined events of outstanding achievement on three fronts.

For BP and its partners, development of the Andrew field's facilities represents an enormously successful venture, exceeding even the most challenging project targets set within a stringent economic climate. From its seemingly defiant position over a twenty year period during which the field was characterised by a refusal to yield acceptable financial returns under any of several proposed development plans, Andrew has been turned around to begin a positive future as a profitable producing asset.

For the wider oil and gas industry, both in the North Sea and internationally, Andrew presents a clear demonstration of the synergy which can result from companies working together in a well-structured alliance clearly focused on a common business goal. The aspiration to establish a culture whereby oil companies and contractors share the risks and rewards of their joint endeavours has been brought to fruition, providing financial gains for all involved.

As its third measure of success, Andrew stands as a remarkable tribute to what can be achieved, indeed brought into the realms of possibility, by the sheer enthusiasm and commitment of individuals once they are freed from the constraints of traditional behaviour. The project has unlocked innate personal abilities and accessed previously untapped potential, revealing a natural desire for co-operation and driving the project team to set and surpass new levels of performance.

This story is an invitation to share the experiences of the Andrew project, relating how the alliance was formed and stepped away from 'business as usual' for the design, construction and completion of the field's facilities. How problems were overcome when they arose, to bring the field on stream more than six months early and over £80 million under budget. How the team delivered a North Sea development project which must surely be classed as an extraordinary business result.

Author's note

The origins of this book lie in a request from BP and its development partners to capture and record the experiences gained during the creation of the platform and subsea facilities for the Andrew and Cyrus fields. The resulting story has been produced in anticipation that the lessons learned from the project's unconventional approach will be of interest to all participants in the Andrew development, and hopefully to others in the oil industry.

No business as usual deals with the Andrew project from the presanction period to the production of first oil. While the work focuses on the Andrew facilities alliance, the project acknowledges that many others have made significant contributions to the overall development of the field, particularly in the areas of commercial activity and subsurface engineering which began early in the development programme and have continued to the present day. The successful completion of the fields' facilities and first wells represents only the beginning of the life cycles for Andrew and Cyrus, which throughout the coming years of production are expected to continue as a sound business investment.

The information for *No business as usual* was researched and gathered throughout a period of twelve months, working alongside members of the Andrew project team at design and construction sites, and during offshore installation. In-depth interviews provided input from all sectors of the alliance: from managers, engineers, and designers; fabricators, welders, pipefitters and electricians; commissioning and operations teams; planners, secretaries and administrators, to mention but some. Equipment suppliers, certifying authority and corporate executives were also included.

In all, the experiences of over one hundred and twenty people helped to create this portrayal of the Andrew facilities development. As such, the story is a cross section of perspectives and as far as possible, an independent view of the project's actions and accomplishments. It does not attempt to relate every event which occurred, but focuses on those aspects of technology and behaviour which maintained Andrew on the road to success.

To capture the lessons learned for the benefit of the wider industry, the story is told openly, describing both the behavioural changes and the problems which were encountered along the way. Above all it is a story of people and their interactions, and their unanimously positive response to the enjoyment gained through contributing to Andrew's achievements.

Part one

Building the alliance

'We were seeking team players,
not spectators. If Andrew was to
succeed, it had to be a team game'

John Martin
Project manager BP

Andrew Development

supplier information pack

BP

The need for change

'We had learned that only by setting seemingly impossible targets would we begin the process of change that was required'

Colin Maclean
Manager of programmes BP

In 1990 BP Exploration was embarked on a journey of radical change. Across the spectrum of its operations, the very foundations of the way the company conducted its oil and gas business were being questioned. While the organisation had grown in size, a widening diversity of interests and the legacy of traditional practice had led to inefficiency and reduced profit margins. New initiatives, many of them demanding a fundamental cultural shift, were set in motion to revitalise the company, sharply focusing on ways to improve profitability against a backdrop of tightening economic margins in the oil and gas industry. Increased returns on investment were imperative.

In BP's principal area of upstream activity in the North Sea, the days of large oil discoveries had given way to an era of smaller fields with marginal economics. The demand to reduce development costs in the region had come under further pressure as new provinces around the globe were beginning to present attractive investment opportunities in direct competition for oil company capital. The combined effects were threatening not only BP's business ventures and those of other operating companies, but also placed in jeopardy the survival of the North Sea as a leading oil producing region.

To strengthen the foundations of BP's long term future and simultaneously demonstrate that continuing prosperity in the North Sea was possible, the company recognised it needed to set far more challenging business targets for capital development projects. Included among its strategic responses were the cutting of capital development costs by thirty percent, minimising the size of the company's project teams, and the requirement that new fields should show a twenty five percent rate of return on investment.

'We had learned that only by setting seemingly impossible targets would we begin the process of change that was required,' observes Colin Maclean, then manager of programmes for BP Exploration. 'At that stage the method for achieving these goals was not apparent, but we did realise that we could not rely on our past experience. To follow along the 'business as usual' route would only serve to emphasise what was *not* possible.'

In order to put the ideas into practice, BP reviewed its portfolio of North Sea prospects – 'a cupboard full of morsels and stale crusts,' recalls Maclean. The decision was made to take one of the more problematic prospects and convert it into a flagship for BP's new way of doing business. The theory was that if an unpromising offshore prospect could be turned around and developed into a viable producing asset, it would boost confidence and stimulate other activities across the industry. The 'guinea pig' in the experiment was to be the Andrew field.

Semisubmersible drilling rig *Sea Quest* drilled the Andrew discovery well.

Andrew, named after the patron saint of Scotland, was discovered in 1974 on acreage awarded in the third UK licensing round, lying some 230km northeast of Aberdeen in Block 16/27a. Appraisal drilling over the following eight years revealed a relatively small and complex reservoir, extending into Block 16/28, with a thin oil column, large gas cap and extensive water leg. BP also holds the operating licence for adjacent Block 16/28, containing the smaller Cyrus reservoir some 10km to the north.

Between 1981 and 1988 Andrew was put forward as a development contender on a number of occasions, only to be returned to the shelf as commercially unattractive. A range of development scenarios – including a minimum facilities platform plus subsea wells, semisubmersible installations and fixed production platforms – all failed to meet the economic targets of the day. In addition to complexities in producing the reservoir, limited infrastructure in the area at that time created difficulties with sale of the associated gas. A further blow to the field's future came with the oil price collapse of 1986. It appeared that the equation for bringing Andrew forward was to remain unsolved.

'The on-and-off nature of Andrew over a sixteen year period served to heighten the challenge we set ourselves,' notes Maclean. 'Now, at a time when oil prices were around $14 a barrel, we were asking for a 25% return on capital from a reservoir which had steadfastly refused to show positive economics. Many of BP's senior managers had by this time worked on the field's development plans at some stage in their careers; when we announced to them Andrew was to become a breakthrough project, the idea was met with knowing looks of sympathy.'

Despite doubts in some quarters, the project demonstrated from the outset that BP was intent on moving away from its past approach. The small company team which was to carry out preliminary development work was fully integrated, aimed at bringing together disciplines which had previously exhibited a form of territorial adversity.

'The formation of a team which combined engineering, subsurface and commercial interests was an essential element in setting us off on a different track,' says BP project co-ordinator Paul Bibby. 'We had never experienced this degree of integration before. Once the old barriers to openness and clarity were broken down, the resulting dialogue and understanding gave us the opportunity to determine the real cost drivers on the project. It may seem an obvious move in retrospect, but it was a very different style of problem solving for BP six years ago.'

Working together on those key cost drivers, the team reviewed the possible options for Andrew's development, conscious of the need to choose an optimised solution which would balance the requirements of reservoir and facilities engineers.

The need for change

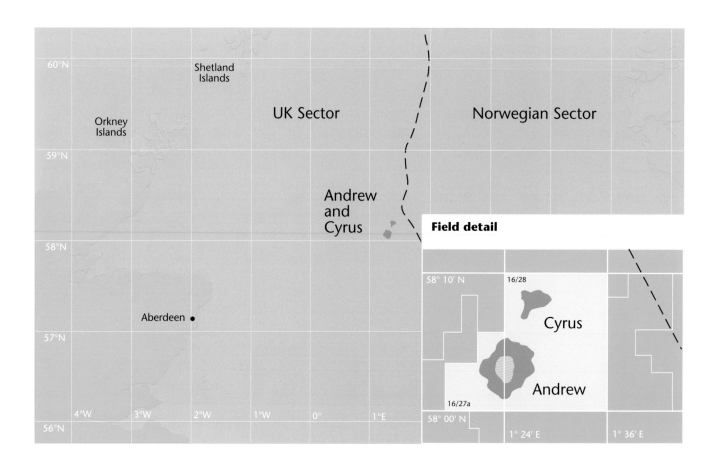

A critical step, achieved through close co-operation, was the determination of the preferred gas management plan incorporating gas export and reinjection. This had a major bearing on the field's production facilities, which in the process were optimised based on a production, drilling and quarters platform. Andrew's final appraisal well was also being planned at this time.

Over the course of 1991 the conceptual platform design was further defined in co-operation with a leading engineering contractor. But by the end of that period, the cost estimate for developing the facilities stood at around £450 million – still too high to meet BP's financial targets.

'Although we had made a beginning along the right road, it became clear that something extra was needed to bring Andrew within sanctionable reach,' explains BP project manager John Martin. 'Applying the latest technology was a vital part of the equation, but this alone could not achieve the reductions in capital expenditure necessary for the project to receive the go-ahead.

'An even more radical formula was called for, a complete departure from the usual style of oil industry contracting, one which required a step change in behaviour,' he emphasises. 'The adversarial relationships between oil companies, contractors and suppliers had to be confined to the history books – we believed that only by working in close alignment with our contractors could we hope to make Andrew a success. To this end, behaviour was identified as the essential partner for technology, the twin building blocks which if brought together could be capable of producing an extraordinary result.'

A vision for Andrew

Early in 1992, BP regrouped to plan the next phase of attack on Andrew's stubborn resistance to compliance with a viable economic solution.
The formulation of a strategy which would take the project forward for eventual sanction by BP and its licence partners was under way.

The idea of behavioural change as an essential ingredient for success had taken hold, reinforced by feedback from BP's Hyde project which was beginning to suggest that the much discussed merits of alliance working, if managed correctly, could bear fruit.

'Hyde demonstrated important aspects of alliancing but on a smaller scale,' observes John Martin. 'While we recognised that some form of co-operative client-contractor relationship held the key to the way forward for Andrew, it was also clear that simply bringing contractors onboard in the traditional manner under normal contractual agreements was unlikely to provide the additional impetus necessary to drive down the project's costs. We had tried that before and adversity followed.'

Additional evidence supporting the case for creating a more co-operative contractual environment came from BP's Bruce project. During the construction of the platform's 8000t cellar deck by Trafalgar House Offshore Fabricators in Teeside, it was realised that traditional working practices had finally led to the imbalanced situation where there were more men working 'back in the office' than at the fabrication workface on the cellar deck. In response, BP's construction manager John O'Brien and Trafalgar House project manager Alex Dawson concluded that real cost savings could be gained by redressing the balance and together had begun implementing a more co-operative and efficient programme for fabrication.

The vision then emerging for Andrew was that BP and the projects's major contractors, which were yet to be selected, should be aligned not only towards common objectives, but also with shared business interests in the project's success, firmly linking profitability to performance. In addition, a further challenge would be to try to enroll members of the project team in the drive toward cost reduction.

Andrew key facts	
Discovered	
1974	
Location	
UK Blocks 16/27a and 16/28. 230km northeast of Aberdeen	
Water depth	
115m	
Reservoir	
Palaeocene sandstone with associated gas cap. Approximately 2500m below sea level	
Recoverable reserves	
Estimated 112 million barrels oil and 3.8 billion cubic metres gas	

'An even more radical formula was called for, a complete departure from the usual style of oil industry contracting'

John Martin
Project manager BP

The need for change
A vision for Andrew

Andrew declaration

In every respect the Andrew development will be the most successful oilfield investment on the United Kingdom Continental Shelf to date.

We assert that through the design and creation of powerful relationships and commitments, we will achieve an extraordinarily successful outcome for BP, partners, contractors, suppliers and all who contribute.

We offer an opportunity for the industry to share the challenge we have set ourselves, to create new performance standards and thereby transform the efficiency and profitability of our business.

The Andrew Team

That enrolment should also function at all levels in the project, rather than be confined to upper management and corporate boards – a 'top down' commitment. By aligning individuals to the project's goals, encouraging them to challenge costs, seek best value and implement innovation, Andrew would provide a climate which would both cultivate behavioural change and promote technical excellence. To back up its growing commitment to these ideals the team issued an unequivocal declaration of intent that Andrew would be the most successful offshore oilfield investment in the UK to date.

In analysing the weaknesses of the established 'business as usual' approach, BP was aware of its own shortcomings as a client oil company. The contractual adversity experienced in past projects had largely arisen from the custom of the client controlling each of its contractors in a compartmentalised fashion, thereby creating self-interest groups operating in isolation and fuelling the perceptions that other contractors' needs were being placed ahead of theirs.

The presence of large client teams to oversee all contractor activities and administer prescriptive procedures fostered further mistrust, in the process blocking opportunities for innovation and stultifying desires on both sides to strive for more economic solutions. As trust diminishes, communication fades, visibility reduces and problems can remain undetected until a late stage, causing schedules to slip and translate into cost overruns. Financial claims and counterclaims have been the trademarks of many North Sea projects in the past.

'We were aware that management of the contractual interfaces was frequently a major source of inefficiency and of cost growth,' Martin points out. 'It seemed reasonable to believe that if the stakeholders were given the chance to manage their own interfaces with the support of the client, backed by incentives to motivate this, some of the principal misunderstandings and causes leading to increased costs could be eliminated. We had no proof that this would work; it was a matter of judgment.'

BP's intention to integrate the project team presented a natural continuation of the early predevelopment teamwork. Rather than follow the more usual route where a project's design, fabrication, installation, and commissioning phases are handled by a succession of different contractors – fertile ground for interface problems to flourish – all companies were to take part throughout the project as members of a single fully integrated team. BP's presence was to be minimal, eliminating the duplication of man-for-man marking in favour of 'best man for the job' selection. The operations group which would run the platform was also to participate in the project team from the outset.

'We were seeking team players, not spectators,' emphasises Martin. 'If Andrew was to succeed, it had to be a team game.'

Contractor selection

Although a contracting strategy was beginning to form for the BP project team, broadcasting the message externally about the Andrew initiative was yet to be addressed. In May 1992, BP embarked on a mission to communicate its ideas to the industry's broad spectrum of contracting interests, gathering together the leading companies to explain its ideas for developing Andrew through a new way of working.

The call for a 'behavioural revolution' was greeted with enthusiasm by some contractors, but scepticism from others. Was this just a disguised scheme for operators to put the squeeze on contractors' profit margins? And if the revolution was such a fine idea, why offer a downbeat prospect like Andrew as the basis for what would undoubtedly be a difficult task? One leading contractor summed up the feelings of many by describing Andrew as 'a dog of a project'.

Concerns were not restricted to the contracting sector. 'Doubts were also being raised by BP's licence partners of the time,' remarks Paul Bibby. 'While they were keen to reduce capital cost, some were uneasy at the degree of contractor dependence being proposed by BP. This approach had not been tried before and there were many unanswered questions. We ourselves were not sure of all the steps to get to our goal; we had to hold fast to our vision.'

The team was clear however that it wanted the facilities contractors to be involved in the presanction phase to establish an early sense of ownership in the project and to work on reducing Andrew's unacceptably high facilities cost estimate of £450 million. There was a determination to ensure that major value decisions were made as early as possible. In this regard, the fundamental influence of the engineering design contractor on the outcome of offshore projects was well recognised, leading to the decision to bring the designer on board first and to retain the same company for both preliminary and detailed platform design, thereby removing another potential interface.

To design, build and install Andrew's platform facilities, plus subsea hardware and pipelines, would require the specialist skills of seven contracting companies. Selection of those contractors was to be undertaken in a fundamentally different way by BP. Given that most of the major players under consideration had track records demonstrating technical competence, other parameters had to be brought into the selection process which would help distinguish between contenders not simply on the basis of a commercial bid, but also on less tangible factors associated with company performance, behaviour as members of a team, and commitment to transforming Andrew into a valued asset.

BP moved away from a traditional tendering process and developed a set of ten new criteria, identified as the Minimum Conditions of Satisfaction (MCOS) against which the company would judge prospective candidates, applying these first in the selection of the design contractor.

'The Andrew selection criteria were markedly different,' states Ash Bakshi, who spearheaded the alliance contribution of Brown & Root and acted as Andrew's deputy project manager. 'At first there were many discussions and presentations during which we sought clarification of BP's rather alien vocabulary

Alliance contractor selection Ten Minimum Conditions Of Satisfaction (MCOS)	State preparedness for accountability in post start-up and logistics activities
Commitment to £270 million development cost, without reducing profitability of contractors	Pursue design philosophies and standards to deliver a safe, operable minimal intervention platform and minimise asset life cycle costs
Proposal of a commercial basis and accountability for services	Possess a strategy for managing information throughout the lifetime of the field and across all parties involved
Demonstration of continuous performance improvement programme	Eliminate inefficiencies at all interfaces
Confirm availability of key personnel and their personal commitment to efficiency of the development. Abide by BP's Offshore Contractor's Charter covering the working environment and respect for individuals	Establish relationships with suppliers and subcontractors which are aligned with the project's philosophy and which result in significant reductions in cost and delivery periods. The procurement process will produce quality and reliability, complete delivery, and will recognise BP's obligation to comply with European Community legislation.
Adopt company quality and safety management systems which contain self-regulating mechanisms	

about 'demonstrating commitment'. The fact that BP was prepared to admit it didn't have all the answers to solve Andrew's demands surprised us. When the tender document arrived it was only 50 pages in all – the slimmest we'd ever received – and totally non-prescriptive. This left us in no doubt that BP was serious about changing the nature of the business.'

From its experience of past project inefficiencies Brown & Root identified several major areas where the project could make savings with the potential to reduce capital expenditure by at least 20%. In keeping with the open and questioning philosophy of the project, Brown & Root was also invited to stipulate its own minimum requirements of BP's performance, effectively reversing the MCOS process. Among those conditions the company requested that BP's team be limited in size to less than 20 people, and called for equality across the project for oil company and contractor personnel.

'As part of our submission we were also asked to put forward a proposal for the commercial basis for our role in the alliance,' adds Bakshi. 'We took the opportunity to offer a plan which demonstrated how all participants could share in a risk and reward scheme with the chance of increased profits, determined by the project's final outturn cost. This was to form the foundation of the Andrew gainshare mechanism.'

At the end of 1992 Brown & Root's proposals were successful in securing contractual responsibility for Andrew's topsides, jacket and subsea design, plus procurement and project management support. The selection was based on the ten MCOS alone and, most unusually, did not include a commercial evaluation. The company's understanding of BP's goals and the matching of two people-centred company cultures paved the way for a strong and continuously evolving relationship, one which was to prove fundamental to Andrew's success.

Together the two companies' team members set about the task of promoting the Andrew initiative – 'selling the concept' as Bakshi puts it – to other potential contractors who were likely to contribute further value to the project.

In addition to the ten MCOS, the candidates were judged on commercial and technical input, all issues receiving predetermined weightings. In some areas the MCOS dominated, particularly for high risk elements such as the platform's topsides where successful company interfaces would be essential; in others, cost and technical capability were the main criteria. The key to the assessments was to establish which companies exhibited a healthy balance between sound commercial tenders and firm commitment to the project's goals, rather than applying the commonly used yardstick of simply selecting the lowest priced bid. Furthermore, contractors were also asked to recognise and acknowledge that in an alliance, company profits could also potentially be placed at risk.

Brown & Root's proposed areas for capital expenditure savings

Reduce client personnel by combining resources of BP, contractors and suppliers

Avoid fabrication growth caused by late design changes and equipment deliveries

Adequate project duration for design innovation

Improve supplier relationships, use standard products and functional specifications, reduce documentation

Minimise field inspection and expediting

'The fact that BP was prepared to admit it didn't have all the answers to solve Andrew's demands surprised us'

Ash Bakshi
Deputy project manager
Brown & Root

The need for change
Contractor selection

Contractors displayed understandable caution in the process, particularly over joint accountability for the overall cost. For one of the MCOS, a development cost of £270 million had been set as an extreme target to gauge the companies' commitment to cost reduction; the low figure also served as a signal to reinforce the message that a step change was needed, not simply a 'chipping away' at cost on a small scale. As individual contractors would be working under different methods of financial payment – reimbursed costs with fixed profits and overheads and fixed lump sums were the two principle methods involved – there was initial concern that although joint commitment was required under a risk and reward gainshare system, one party might not have influence over the actions of another in achieving the target cost. This was a clear sign that mutual trust, a rare commodity in the 'business as usual' environment, would not appear automatically for Andrew on the strength of its stated ideals alone; that trust would have to grow.

As the selection process gathered momentum and open dialogue increased, suspicion and resistance began to be displaced by growing optimism for the Andrew approach. 'It was a process of enrolment in the Andrew vision,' declares Bakshi.

Following soon after Brown & Root, Santa Fe became the next company to join the team. The importance of selecting a single drilling contractor to design, build and operate the platform's drilling rig – albeit for the operational phase not until several years hence – was seen as a vital move that should be conducted early in the programme to create ownership. This would also eliminate the interfaces associated with the more traditional approach of choosing a different contractor for each of these activities.

'Santa Fe was firm in the view that the most economic way to supply Andrew's drilling module was for BP to state only basic requirements, against which they would provide a fit-for-purpose rig,' explains Bibby. 'We had to agree to trust their better judgment and experience, which we did. We found this refreshing – we were learning to accept that such moves were necessary if Andrew was to obtain a different result.'

Over the course of the next several months the other team members came on board, each company taking part in the selection of its successors. By September 1993, Saipem, Trafalgar House Offshore Fabricators (now Trafalgar John Brown), Highlands Fabricators (now BARMAC, a joint venture company formed between Brown & Root and McDermott Marine Construction), Emtunga and Allseas had claimed their places in the Andrew team, working under individual contracts which would reimburse their manhours expended during the presanction stage. The primary task now was to produce a target cost for the project that all parties were committed to, a cost which was not padded with overestimation and contingency, but one which was balanced between providing profit for the participants and gaining sanction from the development partners.

'We had to agree to trust their better judgement and experience, which we did'

Paul Bibby
Project co-ordinator BP

Presanction

For the ensuing two months the alliance worked towards finalising the presanction estimate for the Andrew facilities development. Front end engineering design had already been started in February 1993 by Brown & Root in London; as successive members of the alliance joined the project, each company provided key staff to the team to begin contributing experience and new ideas to bring down Andrew's capital cost.

Individuals recall the period as one of intensity. An integrated management team comprising the seven contractors' alliance managers and led by BP's project manager, had been set up to run the project. Bringing together a group of major contractors, including some which under normal business conditions viewed each other as competitors, seemed likely to create tensions.

'Preparing the presanction estimate was an early test of the co-operation we had all been talking of for months,' says Tony Press, alliance manager for installation contractor Saipem. 'At first we were cautious. Some of the old prejudices were evident – we still encountered the attitude of 'look out for the installation contractor'. But by working together on the estimate these were eroded away as we came to understand one another's methods and recognised the prize could only

The need for change
Presanction

Clarity on the precise content of contractors'
estimates was essential

be won by a genuine joint effort. This was the time when that previously elusive
trust factor began to grow between us.'

The process was nonetheless a demanding one. At the heart of the exercise
was an agreement to challenge and interrogate suggestions as they came forward,
including a mutual review of contractors' bid prices, a move which had been
inconceivable before. 'The policy was to attack what would hinder us and foster
that which would benefit,' emphasises Brian Colpitts, alliance manager for
integrated deck fabricator TJB. 'Our bids were already tight; finding ways to
reduce them still more was a serious challenge.'

The team was seeking more than just an estimate; the aim was a comprehensive
target cost which was not concealing any surprises. For this all parties were
required to be totally open about their scopes of work and methods, and were
soon to realise that the old habit of building-in added contingencies had to be
eliminated, as all participants would stand or fall as a single entity on the value
of the sanction price. Clarity on the precise content of the estimates was essential.

'The incentives for performing in this way became clear to everyone,' John
Martin points out. 'The financial rewards of a large North Sea project could
possibly be drawn within our reach, and furthermore, if we were able to succeed
with Andrew, it would provide many valuable business lessons for the future
benefit of all the participants.'

The team was driving towards a platform design based on a single lift
integrated deck of around 10,250t supported by a four-legged steel jacket of 7500t
with 16 piles, and a pre-installed six-slot drilling template. Compared with the
earlier pre-engineering conceptual design, the two structures were considerably
lighter, providing savings in structural steel and fabrication. But more significantly
in the case of the topsides, an integrated deck of this size could be built and

completed onshore and installed in a single lift by Saipem's *S7000* vessel, yielding both economic and practical advantages compared with the earlier design approach of fabricating multiple modules requiring several lifts and an extensive period of offshore hookup and commissioning.

Oil export, scheduled to begin in January 1997 and plateau at 70,000 barrels of oil per day (bpd), was planned via the existing Forties system to Cruden Bay in Scotland, requiring a new 16km long connecting pipeline from Andrew. Earlier in the year, the revised gas management scheme had increased the field's recoverable reserves and presented the opportunity to offer the gas for sale at attractive commercial prices. At presanction stage, gas export had been narrowed down to two gas trunkline options, either via the SAGE (Scottish Area Gas Evacuation) system to St. Fergus in Scotland, or through CATS (Central Area Transmission System) to Teesside.

Andrew's subsurface team, led by reservoir engineers Peter Smith and Trevor Garlick, had succeeded in steering the project towards investigating the potential of horizontally drilled wells to tap the field's reserves more effectively. A successful horizontal appraisal well completed early in 1993 demonstrated that the number of wells required could be reduced from nineteen to twelve by opting for horizontal rather than vertical wells.

Presanction effort began to take off. The inclusion of fabrication, drilling and installation contractors in the design team permitted a range of co-operative measures to be proposed and explored.

Scopes of work were exchanged between designer and fabricators, aimed at achieving the most efficient production of construction drawings by using state-of-the-art 3D CAD technology and electronic drawing transfer to sites; low pre-heat welding techniques and other construction measures were adopted to make the designs more 'fabrication friendly', with TJB's preferred build method for the integrated deck influencing design decisions.

Duplication of effort was also attacked, with BARMAC and Saipem agreeing to use common grillage for loadout and transportation of the jacket. Saipem also contributed several proposals which would help configure the structures to the capabilities of the *S7000* and save on platform installation, including the reuse of existing padeyes and lifting beams.

BARMAC offered to roll steel tubulars for TJB, which in turn would fabricate a stairtower for Santa Fe's drilling module. Accommodation module supplier Emtunga and Brown & Root were able to combine sourcing of materials to secure reduced prices. Pipelines installer Allseas provided guidance on more compact designs for pipeline tie-ins.

The procurement of Andrew's equipment and materials also came under close scrutiny. The project's commitment to minimising field inspection, eliminating expediting,

'By working together on the sanction estimate the old prejudices were eroded away'

Tony Press
Alliance project manager Saipem

The need for change
Presanction

'Our bids were already tight; finding ways to reduce them still more was a serious challenge'

Brian Colpitts
Alliance project manager TJB

pursuing functional specifications and reducing vendor documentation, led to a radically new strategy for interacting with suppliers. The 15 major package suppliers were identified and aligned with Andrew's goals at an early stage. Total acquisition cost for equipment and materials was aimed to be reduced by 30% across the project.

Rather than being required to work to a pressured fast track schedule, contractors were allowed the time to pursue detailed assessments of the scope of work, as BP contracts manager Bob Campbell explains. 'Making time to permit a thorough front end evaluation was the foundation for the project. Historically BP would appoint a lead contractor, work out an estimate and receive sanction, and then go out to tender. Invariably the budget prices would come in well above the estimate. For Andrew we were determined to arrive at a more focused estimate; with sufficient time to advance the project concept the team was able to achieve this, adjusting tender stage budget prices as the design began to take shape.'

The presence of only thirteen BP personnel integrated into the team reinforced the fact that Andrew was taking a very visible step away from 'business as usual' involving large client teams. Without man-for-man marking, individuals quickly discovered they had to adjust from normal project behaviour patterns and take responsibility for their own decisions instead of seeking client review and approval for even the most minor issues. By setting people free to determine their own actions and targets, rather than these being rigorously imposed by the client, accountability and commitment grew as the players identified with Andrew and forged themselves into a unit.

As the advantages of working openly together became more apparent, increasing enthusiasm fuelled the alliance to resolve remaining interface problems and promoted further innovative thinking. The seeds were being firmly sown for what was later to become known as the 'Spirit of Andrew', a principle, based on trust, that the alliance companies would put the best interests of the project ahead of purely self-centred gains. The impetus established during presanction proved to be only a beginning and was to gather even greater momentum as the project progressed, delivering unexpected savings across the development.

Sanction and gainshare

By November 1993 the target cost was finalised. The alliance put forward a detailed estimate for delivering the Andrew platform and pipeline facilities for £373 million with first oil to be produced at the beginning of 1997. The figure was based on a work estimate of £334 million plus a contingency sum of £39 million as unallocated provision. Compared with the previous estimate of £450 million, the alliance was effectively committing to slice almost 20% off Andrew's development cost.

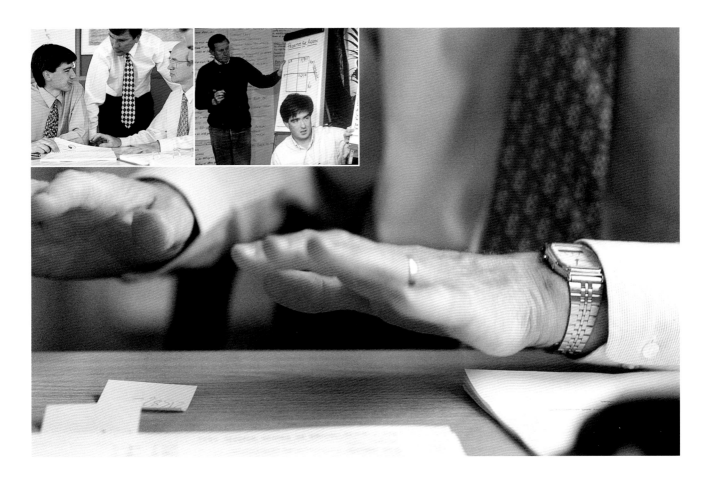

The estimate was subjected to an independent check by BP's cost and risk analysts. While the economics appeared to provide an attractive rate of return, the conclusion was that the Andrew facilities had only a 38% probability of being completed within the estimate of £373 million when compared with historical cost data for the North Sea.

More typically BP would expect at least 50% probability of achieving the target set at sanction. This placed Andrew well outside the risk comfort zone, a factor which created initial resistance to the project plan in some quarters within BP and led to expectations that the development would overrun its budget. Traditionally extra cost would be borne solely by the client, but in an unequivocal move away from 'business as usual' the alliance companies had also proposed that under the project's risk and reward approach they would share such an overrun should it occur, up to a cost of £50 million. At this higher figure of £423 million, Andrew's chances of achieving production on schedule rose to 80% – but at this level, contractors' profits would be outweighed by their expenditure.

This emphatic statement of commitment by the alliance, backed by support from BP Exploration's top executives John Browne and Chris Gibson-Smith, helped win sanction for Andrew from the BP board in February 1994.

'People felt a little nervous about the relatively low cost level of £373 million – we even had doubts ourselves'

Colin Maclean
Andrew asset manager BP

The need for change
Sanction and gainshare

Andrew development partners	
BP Exploration	62.75%
LASMO	16.21%
Mitsubishi Oil	11.18%
Clyde Petroleum	6.66%
Talisman Energy	3.20%

'Achieving sanction was not an easy process,' recounts Colin Maclean, now BP's asset manager for Andrew. 'This way of doing business was radically different for BP and not surprisingly attracted criticisms when it was first proposed. People felt a little nervous about the relatively low cost level of £373 million – we even had doubts ourselves.'

Those doubts had been brought sharply into focus immediately before sanction when three of BP's development partners – Agip, British Gas and Fina – sold their stakes in the Andrew licence. 'We were concerned about the move at the time,' admits Maclean. 'Andrew's market value had improved as sanction appeared imminent and hence it was perhaps timely to trade assets, but it caused us to consider whether we were correct in our judgments. The fact that other companies were highly enthusiastic about the Andrew approach and were ready to take up the challenge immediately, was of great encouragement.'

Joining BP and its remaining partner from the original licence group, LASMO, were Mitsubishi Oil Exploration, Clyde Petroleum, and Talisman Energy (at that time as Goal Petroleum). The licence group remains unchanged to the present day, endorsing the project's philosophy and aims in a confident demonstration of close support for BP and the alliance partners.

Each of the alliance contractors entered into an individual commercial contract with BP, against well defined scopes of work, totalling some £217 million. Payment methods followed one of two main types: either as manhours reimbursed at cost with fixed overhead and profit, or as fixed lump sum contracts with milestone dates. In addition, the cost of as yet unawarded elements – equipment and materials, jacket piles and predrilling template, offshore hookup and commissioning, and construction insurance – were included along with BP's own management costs, to reach the work estimate.

Included in each company's cost estimate was a profit element which would be secure if the project met the target cost. But under Andrew's risk and reward philosophy – the gainshare mechanism – that profit would be jeopardised if the alliance failed to meet the target. Conversely, the gainshare also presented the opportunity for enhancing contractors' profits by beating the target, which for BP and the development partners would lead to further reductions in the bottom line for Andrew's facilities.

'The gainshare principle provides the possibility of netting extra benefits,' explains John Martin. 'But this is firmly tied to the alliance performing collectively to beat the target cost. It is structured so that companies will either win or lose together. There can be no finger pointing – success or failure is a joint responsibility.'

Andrew facilities
Target cost breakdown at sanction

Workscope	Contractor	Contract type	£ million (all figures valued at fourth quarter 1993)
Design, procurement and management support	Brown & Root	*Fixed overhead and profit with manhours reimbursed at cost*	36.9
Integrated deck fabrication	TJB	*Fixed overhead and profit with manhours reimbursed at cost*	53.8
Jacket fabrication	BARMAC	*Fixed overhead and profit with manhours reimbursed at cost*	20.0
Platform installation	Saipem	*Fixed lump sum*	32.5
Pipelines	Allseas	*Lump sum plus schedule of rates*	39.6
Drilling module	Santa Fe	*Lump sum (engineer, procure, construct)*	28.0
Accommodation module	Emtunga	*Lump sum (engineer, procure, construct)*	5.6
Alliance contractors' total			**216.4**
BP management and third party costs			16.0
Contracts remaining to be awarded at sanction: Equipment and materials for topsides, jacket, piles and template			66.5
Offshore hookup and commissioning			23.7
Fabrication of foundation piles and template			6.6
Construction all risks insurance			5.0
Work estimate			**334.2**
Contingency (unallocated provision)			38.8
Target cost			**373.0**

In a radical departure from conventional project practice, the alliance contractors were asked to take responsibility for a percentage share of any cost savings or overruns that Andrew might potentially produce. The original commercial proposals put forward by Brown & Root called for the total share to be borne by the contractors to amount to at least 50%, but on the first pass this level was not achieved. Although the gainshare had the potential to push up profits, many of the contractors at that stage were focused more on the risk factor than the possible rewards, further confirmation that the £373 million target cost was a genuinely tight budget and was not padded with hidden contingencies. Encouragement from Brown & Root led to an increased uptake by the contractors totalling 54%.

In essence the gainshare meant that if the Andrew facilities were delivered for less than £373 million, the contractors and BP along with its partners would split the savings – including the unallocated provision – in the ratio 54% to 46%. On the downside, if cost overruns occurred, the joint exposure was capped at

'There can be no finger pointing – success or failure is a joint responsibility'

John Martin
Project manager BP

Alliance shares of risk and reward
Total risk (£million)

Contractor	Share %	Total Risk (£ million)
Brown & Root	22	11.0
TJB	12	6.0
BARMAC	6	3.0
Saipem	6	3.0
Allseas	4	2.0
Santa Fe	3	1.5
Emtunga	1	0.5
Alliance contractors' total	**54**	**27.0**
BP and partners	**46**	**23.0**
Total joint exposure to risk under gainshare		**50.0**

£50 million, a figure set to equate to total contractor risk of £27 million, with BP and the partners at risk for the remaining £23 million. Beyond this figure, any additional overrun would be carried by the oil companies.

The combination of relatively standard commercial contracts working alongside the gainshare agreement provided a key motivation for the alliance from the outset. In addition to securing normal profit, the alliance members knew that a much larger financial prize was a possibility, but were also aware that only exceptional performance would attain this.

At the level of individuals working in the team, the freedom to behave openly in a stimulating and co-operative environment had already revealed a glimpse of its potential during presanction. Now the gainshare looked likely to provide the vital commercial incentives at the corporate level. There was optimism within the alliance that together these ingredients could act as a catalyst, an untried key for unlocking the door to performance improvement. But even the most optimistic minds could not have imagined the degree of improvement to come. The alliance was now moving into action to deliver a most extraordinary result.

Gainshare principle

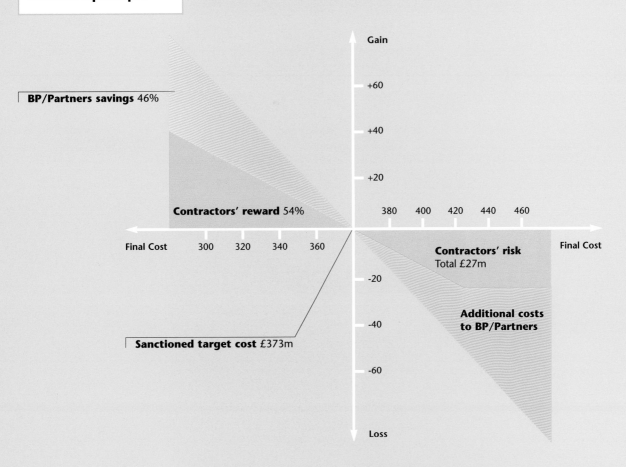

BP/Partners savings 46%

Gain

+60

+40

+20

380 400 420 440 460

Final Cost

Contractors' reward 54%

Final Cost 300 320 340 360

Contractors' risk
Total £27m

-20

Sanctioned target cost £373m

-40

**Additional costs
to BP/Partners**

-60

Loss

Gainshare equities

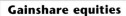

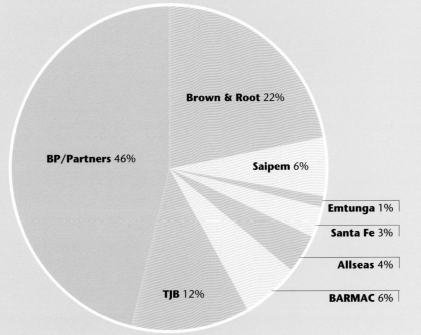

Brown & Root 22%

Saipem 6%

BP/Partners 46%

Emtunga 1%

Santa Fe 3%

Allseas 4%

TJB 12%

BARMAC 6%

The alliance in action

'A culture developed where people set their own targets and then sought ways to improve on them still further'

John Martin
Project manager BP

First moves

With sanction achieved in February 1994, the alliance moved into top gear to begin pursuing the challenging stretched targets it had set during presanction.

In parallel with the drive to reduce target costs, the integrated management team (IMT) had been formulating a strategy for how the alliance would function and interact in readiness for Andrew receiving the go-ahead for development. A non-executive alliance board comprising a senior corporate representative from each of the eight alliance companies was set up outside the day-to-day workings of the project. The purpose of the board was to assist the IMT by giving guidance on the project's direction, as well as maintaining the commitment to Andrew's goals within the corporate organisations.

The alliance was also creating a stronger identity for itself as a unit, defining its role, strategy and principles. These formed the basis for the pioneering Alliance Agreement, formalised at sanction, which was designed to underpin the individual commercial contracts and define the gainshare mechanism.

Andrew alliance principles
Work together in a spirit of openness and co-operation focusing on overall benefit for Andrew as the prime consideration
Use innovative methods to bring the field on stream meeting the design intent and programme at the lowest possible cost below the target
Disclose between alliance members, subject to business confidentiality, respective forward business plan, engineering programme, technical and commercial requirements, and cost information
Commit to achieving effective interfaces between alliance parties, suppliers and subcontractors in all areas of work. Eliminate inefficiency.
Acceptance by each alliance participant of responsibility for management and technical supervision of the services defined in its individual contract
Strive for continuous improvement in all areas through effective business management, engineering excellence and team integration

'The Alliance Agreement was the first of its kind,' says Bob Scott, who together with Steve Willis led the alliance negotiations for BP. 'It took some effort to leave tradition behind and produce a clear, high level document that gathered all interests together under shared responsibility. Before long the benefits of the alliance became so evident that there was no real need to refer to the individual contract documents.'

Contracts manager Bob Campbell reinforces the point: 'There was certainly no adversarial contract waving – you could almost say we put the contracts in a drawer and forgot about them.'

The eight-man IMT led the way into the territory of new contractual relationships by unequivocally declaring its commitment to the project, encapsulating within this the goals of the alliance.

IMT Commitment

The Integrated Management Team is committed to making the Andrew development the most successful project ever in the history of the North Sea.

Working together as a team with aligned objectives, we will strive to reduce costs by delivering Andrew under target budget and ahead of schedule, thus contributing to increased profitability and the long term future for each of the companies participating within the Andrew Alliance.

We will be responsible for the final outcome of the project and as such will ensure that we support one another, avoid duplication of efforts and encourage our teams to share our common objectives

John Martin	BP Exploration
Ash Bakshi	Brown & Root
Brian Colpitts	Trafalgar John Brown
Archie Carmichael	BARMAC
Tony Press	Saipem
Eric Van Baars	Allseas
Oliver Hinton	Santa Fe
Sia Payani	Emtunga

The commitment was to be put to the test in the first weeks of the project. On world markets the oil price had tumbled from $18 to $12 per barrel, causing BP Exploration to require a redistribution of its expenditure over the following two years. The requirement was passed on to the company's assets with the result that Andrew was faced with rescheduling capital expenditure and cash flow from 1994 into 1995.

Together the members of the alliance sought ways to reschedule key events in the programme and defer associated costs. Contributions came from all quarters to meet the challenge. Among the major measures taken were Allseas' offer to continue its proposed early installation of pipelines in 1995 while deferring payment until 1996; Saipem agreed to delay template installation by 12 months to March 1995; and BARMAC rescheduled the start of jacket fabrication from May 1994 until the end of that year, postponing steel delivery and cash outflow.

'Before long the benefits of the alliance became so evident that there was no real need to refer to the individual contract documents '

Bob Scott
BP

First moves

'As people realised they were not constrained by traditional client-contractor hierarchies, their desire to contribute came to the fore'

John Martin
Project manager BP

Assembling and cementing together Andrew's team was seen as fundamental to the success of a project which had at the heart of its philosophy close co-operation and the freedom to challenge traditional methods. The core of the team had been formed during presanction; as new members joined the team they were given an induction into Andrew's goals to align them with the project's vision.

'We sought to create an environment which encouraged individuals to come forward with ideas and question proposals in the knowledge that there would be no adverse reaction, no threat to their security on the team,' explains John Martin. 'As people realised they were able to behave openly and that Andrew was not constrained by traditional client-contractor hierarchies, their desire to contribute came to the fore – contribution was their ticket, their entitlement to be on the team. This led to a sense of shared ownership in the project which fired their enthusiasm to participate even more. A culture soon developed where people set their own targets and then sought ways to improve on them still further; once success followed, it became a habit.'

The London-based project team numbered around 350, fully integrated to incorporate personnel from each of the alliance companies into the Brown & Root management and design function. In keeping with its promise to eliminate man-for-man marking, BP provided only 18 people, in some cases working under the supervision of contractors. Across the project team corporate identities receded as alignment to Andrew's goals strengthened and the vision of interdependence crystallised into reality.

From the outset the team was regularly invigorated by courses and sessions away from the project – 'away days' – which maintained the focus on co-operative behaviour and helped prevent a slide back towards the historical 'business as usual' approach. In addition to helping cement the team together and bring difficulties out into the open, the courses stimulated innovative thinking and spurred the project to stretch its targets still further; the concept of teamwork took on a new and powerful dimension which sustained the efforts of individuals and drove the Andrew development forward.

On previous projects, the functions of cost control, planning and document control had frequently attracted duplication of effort between client and contractors, both in terms of manpower and reporting. But with no separate client team on Andrew to repeat the pattern of inefficiency, a single group was set up which acted as a central resource for the whole project.

'Rather than accumulate all contractors' data, reformat this and then redistribute it as a management overview, a small central team of a dozen people monitored and co-ordinated all the project control functions for the alliance,' reports Andrew commercial manager, Barry Smale.

'Alliance members planned their work with their own corporate systems – there were no prescriptive standards imposed by the project and detailed planning was not duplicated. Nor did we administer contracts in the conventional manner with continuous monitoring, relying instead on initial auditing followed by spot checking contractors' procedures. Progress reporting was limited to a high level monthly cost report rather than very detailed weekly accounts. The overall approach provided greater visibility and very significant savings in manhours and documentation.'

The creation of a detailed computer model of the platform provided a single database to be shared by all contractors.

Information technology played a major part in the project, not only by directly assisting in practical terms for communications and in the production of design and fabrication drawings, but also as an important focal point of co-operation between contractors. Brown & Root's acknowledged position as an industry leader in the development of interactive three dimensional computer aided design tools (3D CAD) was fully exploited to the benefit of the alliance. The creation of a detailed 3D CAD virtual model of the platform provided a single database to be shared by all contractors, reducing by several thousands the number of design manhours expended across the project, and further enabled fabrication shop drawings to be generated directly from the model and electronically transferred to the construction sites.

Although Andrew was seeking and discovering new ways to enhance business efficiency, the door was left open for worthy ideas from the past to make a reappearance. A key example was the reintroduction of budget responsibility officers (BROs), a concept tried several years before by BP and now resurrected to good advantage for Andrew in a modernised format. For each of the alliance contracts, a BRO was appointed to manage the respective interfaces throughout the project, assisting with technical and commercial issues which could have an effect on the smooth running of the alliance.

'This turned out to be a very shrewd move with more beneficial consequences than we first imagined,' observes Bill Ebdon of Brown & Root, BRO for the Andrew jacket. 'During presanction, the BROs had been the leaders of the evaluation teams which had originally chosen the fabrication contractors. This connection was carried forward, growing into a personal commitment – a pride – to ensure the construction phase was delivered successfully. But there were no rules to follow – each BRO had to define his own responsibilities and aims for keeping the contract within budget.'

The role of the BRO was to act as a conduit for promoting the sharing of ideas around the alliance, posing 'what if' questions to stimulate innovative thinking and reporting progress directly to the IMT. Accountability for decisions taken, backed by an understanding of their historical basis, was achieved over the longer term as BROs retained responsibility for their respective areas throughout the project to first oil.

'Each BRO had to define his own responsibilities and aims for keeping the contract within budget'

Bill Ebdon
Jacket BRO Brown & Root

While the BRO concept had its roots in the past, prominent among Andrew's new initiatives was the creation of an ambitious procurement strategy designed to drive out unnecessary costs. The supply of equipment and materials to offshore developments was well recognised as a critical project activity, endowed with a seemingly boundless capacity to throw up damaging problems for project costs and schedule. The potential impact of late and incomplete deliveries on construction programmes was acknowledged to have been the undoing of many previous jobs, disrupting fabrication workflow and commissioning, storing up overrun costs for these later project phases, and fuelling adversarial contractual claims. Within this context, management of the supplier interface had been identified as a key area where valuable improvements could be made, spurring early moves in Andrew's presanction phase.

'Rather than focus primarily on bid prices submitted by package suppliers, the strategy was based upon total acquisition cost,' explains BP's Norman Brown, who as supplier alliance manager developed and spearheaded the initiative together with Brown & Root's materials manager, Peter Jessup.

'The concept is significantly different from considering purchase value alone as it incorporates capital cost of the equipment, associated expenditure incurred by the design contractor in achieving quality and scheduled delivery, and also takes into account the direct influence on fabrication yard costs – the degree of potential carryover work and commissioning effort. We set our sights on achieving total acquisition cost 30% below that of a normal project, without eating into suppliers' profits. This was a step change in performance which would require greater visibility and maximum supplier contribution, supported by a more co-operative relationship between client, contractors and suppliers.'

By following a 'business as usual' approach for procurement, total acquisition costs for Andrew's equipment and materials were estimated at the beginning of the project to total £72 million. Large percentage reductions in this figure clearly had the potential to deliver major cost benefits. To this end, the alliance identified specific activities within the procurement process which were believed likely to yield savings, and devised a proactive programme for enrolling suppliers into the procurement strategy. At around the same time, the UK offshore industry's Cost Reduction Initiative for the New Era (CRINE) was being formulated in detail, and was to provide timely confirmation that the team was on the right track to achieve its goals.

Underlying Andrew's innovative procurement strategy was the project's quality management system (QMS), encompassing all aspects of the development. At its core, the purpose-built system required alliance members and suppliers to demonstrate their own quality assurance plans for acceptance by the project, following which individual companies were entrusted to adhere to a policy of

self-regulation subjected to periodic audits by the Andrew quality team.
The approach constituted a radical break from a tradition founded on extensive
prescriptive demands being placed on suppliers by the client and contractor, backed
up by continuous monitoring and intervention.

'The thrust of the QMS was to encourage companies to take responsibility
themselves for continuous improvement in pursuing best value for Andrew,'
observes quality manager Mike Blyton of Brown & Root. 'At the same time the
alliance committed to eliminating the need for a large project team for expediting
and field inspection duties. Package engineers in the design team acted as the key
interfaces to build working relationships with suppliers, with quality engineers
taking a supporting role – less field surveillance meant we were able to operate
more efficiently with only half the number of quality engineers normally engaged
on a project this size. Tens of thousands of manhours were saved in the process,
while the quality of Andrew as a product is at least equal to that of other North
Sea projects.'

Development of the QMS, vital to Andrew's technical integrity and commercial
success, was running in parallel with the creation of another new and closely
related system, that of safety management. As with all BP projects, safety had been
accorded paramount importance on the Andrew project from its inception, as John
Allinson, BP's leader of the health, safety and environment team, points out.

'Although the development had as its business goal the reduction of capital
costs, the idea that safety and cost could ever be in competition was not a
debatable issue. Safety had the full support of the project's management and of BP

and its partners and assumed primary importance in all cases. There was no possibility of compromise.'

But there were added challenges surrounding the Andrew development in the safety arena. Recent changes to the UK's offshore safety regime had introduced the concept of goal setting regulations, replacing the older prescriptive rules with a risk-based approach to safety. As a cornerstone of the modern safety culture, the industry's newly appointed regulatory body, the Health & Safety Executive, required offshore operators to demonstrate their safety management systems and produce a safety case for all new and existing offshore installations.

'Andrew's timing meant it would be the first fixed manned platform in the industry to require a design safety case, and it would also become the first to undergo the entire safety case process including operations,' adds Allinson. 'As front runner the project team had to interpret new legislation and guidance without any predecessor to refer to, and allow for future legislation that was known to be in the pipeline. It was a period of invention and self-questioning – coupled with Andrew's environment of openness and challenge this led to the raising of ten times the usual number of safety concerns.'

Establishing a safety management system for Andrew was not confined to the London-based project team. All alliance members and suppliers were also embraced by the new legislation, a cultural transition which demanded a demonstration of safety awareness and planning far beyond that of the past.

Closely linked both to Andrew's commitment to enhanced safety and the project's drive toward more efficient quality management, was the early appointment of the certifying authority for the facilities development. In an unusual move for the offshore industry, Lloyd's Register's surveyors had been invited to work alongside the project team from presanction, rather than being 'held at arms length' until the facilities design was well advanced. While maintaining a necessarily independent view in its design appraisal, the certifying authority welcomed the opportunity to participate in the formative stages of the project. By acting as a sounding board for proposed innovations in design and fabrication, the surveyors provided confidence to the team that plans for achieving the statutory Certificate of Fitness were acceptable, and further helped dispel traditional misconceptions about the mass of documentation commonly believed to be necessary for certification.

As an offshore development project, Andrew pursued a life cycle approach, recognising that design of the facilities had a direct and significant influence on the operation of the platform. BP's operations group, which would be responsible for the control and running of the Andrew asset, both on the platform and from its Dyce headquarters in Aberdeen over the field's expected 17-year producing life, formed part of the Andrew team from presanction onwards. In time the entire offshore operations crew, around 70-strong to cover two shifts, was phased into the project as design, fabrication and commissioning progressed. Operations co-ordinator Peter Airey was the first representative to join the Andrew team.

'Historically, operations groups had developed a reputation for changing a platform design after it was completed, to suit their own requirements,' acknowledges Airey. 'Such actions were often viewed as preferential engineering imposed by the client.

'For Andrew we were determined to prevent this cycle being repeated, the effects of which usually start to be felt during fabrication and commissioning. By being in the design team and at the deck fabrication site, operations personnel were able to have direct input to the minimum facilities design, ensuring it incorporated tried and tested features which experience has taught us are valuable, while keeping out unnecessary embellishments. We also assisted with selecting the key package vendors based on life cycle costing, and helped plan the programme leading to onshore commissioning and completion. Input from operations is not unique to Andrew but it has never been carried out to this degree before.'

In due course this involvement was to contribute to Andrew's topsides facilities being totally commissioned and completed onshore with dramatic cost benefits to the project. So advanced was the commissioning programme that the operations crew took up permanent residence in the platform's fully functioning accommodation module four months before sailaway, operating as though offshore. By the time of topsides loadout, the operations team had already accepted Andrew as a working platform.

With the key ingredients of the team brought together, design of Andrew's facilities proceeded apace. The existence of the commercial gainshare mechanism focused minds on co-operating towards a common business goal. With profits and overheads fixed in the platform design contract, the common routine of running up manhours against changing scopes of work offered no additional financial gain, as manpower was reimbursed at cost. The more the project paid out to cover manhours, the less would remain in the potential gainshare pot, a seemingly simple formula which promoted the alignment of team effort towards maximising the possible prize. An outlook of 'doing what's best for Andrew' displaced self-orientated attitudes. Co-operation in determining the most efficient method for achieving goals – undertaken by the alliance company best equipped for the task – became the common currency for the project. 'No contractor sat on the sidelines exhibiting traditional behaviour,' states BP project co-ordinator Paul Bibby. The 'Spirit of Andrew' had quietly established itself as the unseen ninth member of the alliance.

While the gainshare motivated the IMT and senior managers in the project team, there was an early recognition that team members of all disciplines –

'Input from the operations team is not unique to Andrew but it has never been carried out to this degree before'

Peter Airey
Operations co-ordinator BP

'Of course problems occured; the difference was the way people responded'

Steve Brown
Operations manager BP

engineers, draftsmen, supervisors, welders, and secretaries to name but some – should be encouraged and acknowledged for their individual contributions. An Opportunities for Improvement (OFI) scheme was introduced across all phases of the development, designed to stimulate the generation of new ideas and innovations. Over 300 OFIs were raised by individuals and groups, with one third of these receiving awards. Total savings in capital and operating costs originating from OFIs are estimated to be almost £9 million.

But no offshore project, and particularly one so pioneering as Andrew, is without its difficulties. 'Of course problems occurred,' notes Steve Brown, who joined the team as BP operations manager. 'The difference on Andrew was the way people responded.'

One of the first major problems to raise its head post sanction was that of insurance. For the target cost, construction all risks insurance for the facilities had been estimated at £5 million by BP, but by the time the project sought to purchase insurance in the first quarter of 1994, changes in the market place had pushed up costs with the result that Andrew's insurance bill jumped by almost £2 million. This increase was in effect the first 'big hit' on the gainshare and furthermore stemmed from BP, a fact which could have caused discontent among the alliance members. But by now, the alliance – in a clear display of its growing robustness – understood that it would have to shoulder the downside risks of the project as well as share in the possible rewards, leading to acceptance of the increase.

Development of the smaller Cyrus field had been sanctioned by BP along with Andrew

Evidence that the Andrew alliance was beginning to convert the theory of non-adversarial co-operation into beneficial practical results gave impetus to the formation of a second alliance. Development of the smaller Cyrus field, lying 10km to the north in the adjacent BP licence Block 16/28, had been sanctioned by BP along with Andrew.

At that stage a subsea development concept, based on a tie-back to the Andrew platform but not finalised in detail, had been accepted for Cyrus with sanctioned facilities cost of £25.8 million and first oil to be produced concurrent with that from Andrew in 1997. In April 1994, subsea specialist Rockwater was awarded the contract to design, procure and install the Cyrus subsea facilities by BP, with the two companies entering into a 50–50 risk and reward agreement following the principle of Andrew's gainshare mechanism. A further alliance to cover diving work on both projects would bring together the skills of Rockwater and Allseas.

More key alliances were to follow later in the Andrew development. BP joined with four leading contracting companies in the drilling sector to form the industry's first well engineering alliance which predrilled three new template wells for Andrew plus two subsea wells for Cyrus. For operation of the platform including drilling, BP and six contractors forged an operating alliance, supported by suballiances of equipment suppliers and specialist services.

Acting as a focus for the constant push to eradicate unnecessary costs from Andrew's balance sheet, the facilities team had identified key areas of activity considered to be contributors to cost growth on offshore projects. These 'persistent offenders' were to serve as targets for channelling the power now building within the alliance.

As new ideas for attacking costs came forward and successes began to mount, the once daunting challenge of delivering Andrew's facilities for £373 million presented a less onerous prospect. A growing confidence spread through the alliance team that not only could that challenge be met, it could perhaps be surpassed. The culture of setting highly demanding targets without an apparent route or mechanism for achieving these had taken hold. Within only a few months of sanction an emboldened alliance had revised its target commitments: the Andrew team would now aim to deliver the facilities for £320 million and first oil three months early at the beginning of September 1996. The 'Spirit of Andrew' was not only present; it was leading the team to success.

Alliance target areas for savings
Minimise fabrication growth
Delete duplication of effort
Share contractor workscopes to match tasks with best capability
Reduce documentation, expediting and inspection
Use standard products and functional specifications
Foster co-operative relationships between contractors and suppliers
Challenge additional costs which do not add value
Set stretched targets

Jacket, template and piles

At 0345 hours on 8 May 1996, the 6100t Andrew jacket touched down on the seabed in 115m of water following a twelve hour precision operation carried out by Saipem's *S7000* heavy lift crane vessel. With the 134m high jacket structure now docked over the drilling template installed a year earlier, the platform's twelve giant foundation piles would be driven deep into the seabed and grouted into place over the next four days, making the jacket ready to receive Andrew's integrated deck.

Although the field's pipelines, subsea equipment and drilling template had been installed in previous months as scheduled, the jacket provided the first visible evidence that a new platform would soon be taking its place among the North Sea's installations. But the sight of the waiting substructure represented more than a fine engineering achievement. During design, fabrication and installation of the jacket, template and piles, the Andrew alliance had succeeded in cutting the expected £33 million capital cost by more than a quarter; over the preceding two and half years more than £9 million had been contributed to the gainshare.

Design

'Our involvement with the Andrew jacket design was the earliest and most comprehensive opportunity we have yet had to influence the product we were committed to build'

Archie Carmichael
Alliance project manager BARMAC

Throughout the months of 1994, design of the Andrew jacket moved from concept to detail as the alliance companies worked together to optimise the four-legged structure.

The original design concept, based on a 7500t jacket with sixteen piles, was optimised and redesigned into a lighter, simpler design proposed by Brown & Root. The jacket's streamlined tower design is characterised by a cross-braced structure with splayed base section, requiring less perimeter bracing and stiffening, minimising the number of structural nodes and reducing overall steel content.

While the design itself offered savings, the integration of engineers into the team from jacket fabricator BARMAC and installation contractor Saipem helped focus on other design features to make the structure easier to build and install.

'Our involvement with the Andrew jacket design was the earliest and most comprehensive opportunity we have yet had to influence the product we were committed to build,' observes Archie Carmichael, alliance project manager for BARMAC. 'Moreover, early input from all parties was acknowledged to be vital to avoid the traditional clashes known to occur between contractors as particular needs begin to emerge in later stages of the operation – such conflicts had indeed occurred in the past between members of this alliance on other projects. For Andrew the key was to deliver a design which best suited our fabrication methods, and which incorporated the needs of both BARMAC and Saipem in order that changes which commonly arise during construction would be eliminated.'

One prominent example of co-operation across the design-fabrication interface centred on the production of design and construction drawings. Although almost all offshore developments now employ computer aided design (CAD) to generate detailed design drawings, significant additional manhours are often expended at the construction yard in manually extracting information from these to produce a further set of specialised fabrication drawings required to plan and control the building of the jacket. Using Triton, an enhanced version of the proprietary structural software system Euclid, Brown & Root's designers produced a 3D computer model of the jacket from which BARMAC's draftsmen on the team were able to generate fabrication drawings to match the requirements of the workforce at the Nigg construction site. When fabrication began in December 1994, the model was transferred to site to support the construction team.

'Triton effectively enabled us to create the jacket in detail electronically before actually building it in steel,' says jacket BRO Bill Ebdon. 'In addition to achieving a very accurate design in a shorter time, there was no need to produce the normal volume of drawings. A jacket of this size would typically require around 300 primary design drawings, all of which would be redrawn at the fabrication site to produce shop drawings for construction. Instead only 30 or so design drawings were generated for Andrew's jacket, and all shop drawings were taken directly from the model. This saved 12,000 manhours, making it the most extensive and successful practical application of the technique to date.'

Reducing the weight of the jacket and ancillary equipment to cut material and fabrication costs provided a focal point for the alliance contractors.

BARMAC proposed that the completed jacket should be loaded out using trailers rather than by skidding as first envisaged. Under a conventional project approach, the design team would specify the temporary grillage steelwork necessary to support the jacket during fabrication and loadout, while the installation contractor would design additional grillage supports on the transportation barge. But by working together as an integrated team, the three contractors devised a single multipurpose grillage system, reducing temporary steelwork by 300t to 1100t and saving £260,000 in materials, labour and associated civil engineering works.

As the integrated team found its stride in challenging accepted practice, a tide of new ideas began to flow for improving the jacket. Import and export risers were grouped in a single protective caisson to save 120t; mudmat design was simplified

Jacket, template and piles
Design

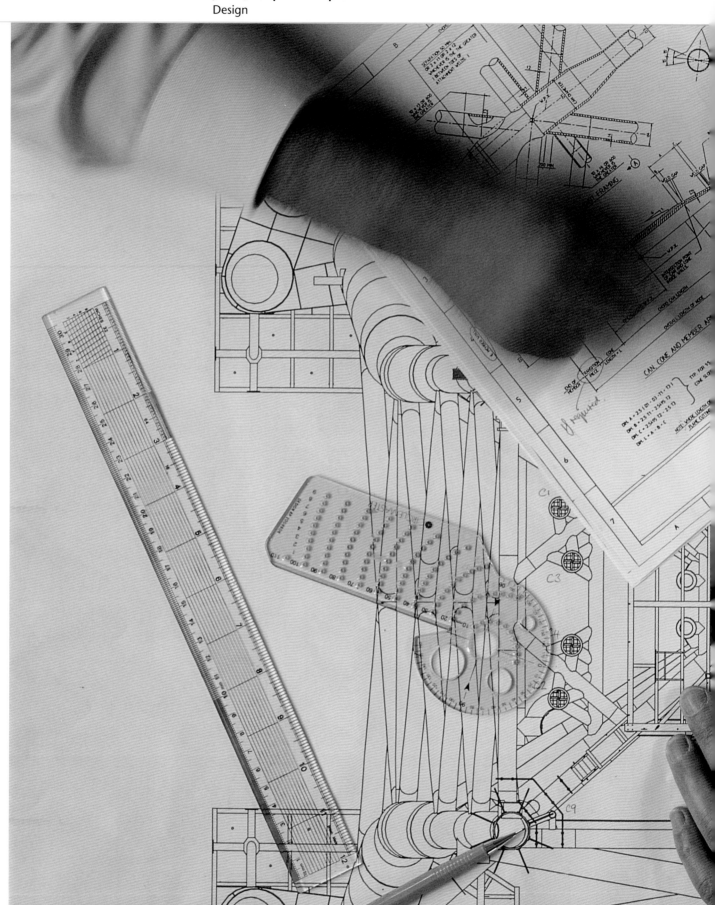

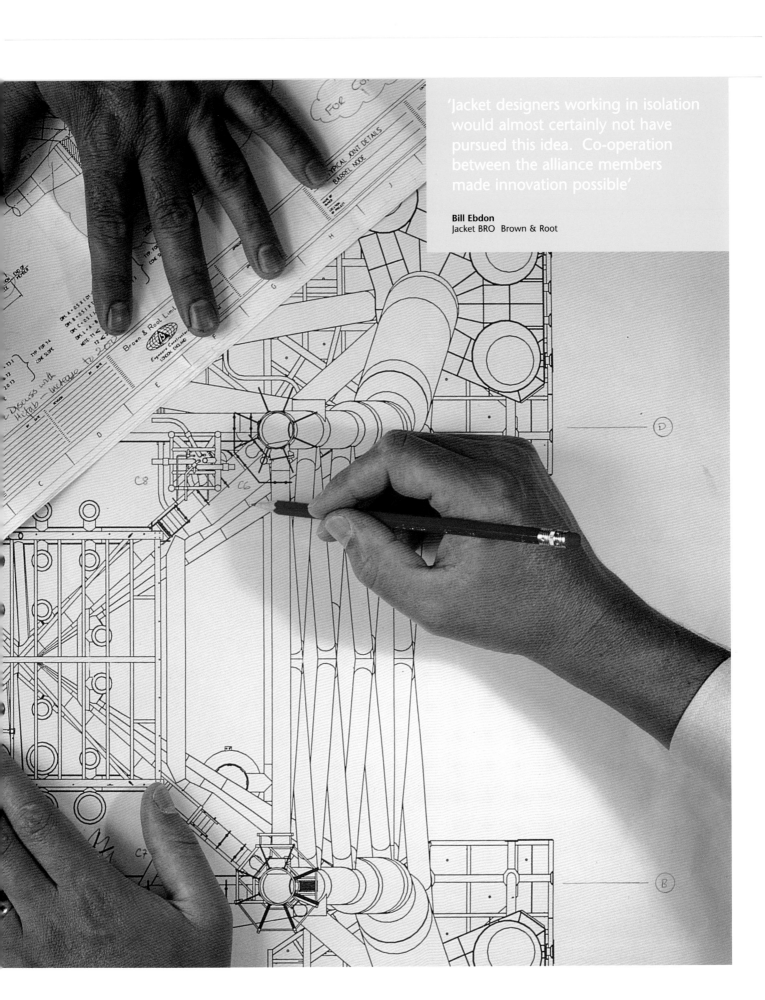

'Jacket designers working in isolation would almost certainly not have pursued this idea. Co-operation between the alliance members made innovation possible'

Bill Ebdon
Jacket BRO Brown & Root

Jacket, template and piles
Design

with the approval of marine warranty surveyor Noble Denton & Associates, saving a further 30t; during fabrication lower preheat temperatures would be used to improve welding conditions; and the jacket would be protected from corrosion by a combination of painting and sacrificial metal anodes.

This latter move encompassed a number of considerations. Rather than follow BP tradition and protect the entire jacket with two coats of black coal tar epoxy paint, for Andrew the jacket would be fully coated by aluminium spray in the splash zone with a single coat of yellow glass flaked paint on the 21,000m^2 surface below. Although this would incur greater capital cost, the coating would be more durable over the life of the platform, reducing operating costs in line with the project's life cycle approach. The selection of yellow was also directly linked to operations, as this would assist visibility in underwater inspection work. But of key importance was that glass flake paint would only be required over ninety percent of the jacket surface, with remaining protection provided by the anodes.

'This had major implications during fabrication,' explains BARMAC's jacket project engineer Gordon Penman. 'As there was sufficient cathodic protection, there was no need to paint the high level closure welds, which meant all painting could be done at ground level before the jacket frames were rolled up, avoiding the erection of complex scaffold platforms. Over 5000 manhours were saved by this means. It is not unusual for painting budgets to double due to high level work.'

Jacket protection systems are also often subjected to inefficient reworking as designs for installation attachments commonly do not appear until fabrication is well advanced. 'Saipem responded to this potential problem by providing detailed designs for the attachments early on – and these did not change later,' says Penman. The installation attachments themselves were also critically reviewed by the integrated team, simplifying lifting sling laydown platforms and re-using lift spreader bars and hydraulic systems supplied by Saipem from previous projects.

The list of cost saving measures for Andrew's jacket grew steadily in the months after sanction, in due course reducing primary steel weight by 560t and secondary steel by 130t to deliver a jacket structure around 6100t. But within the spectrum of jacket innovations, two primary examples stand clear as design breakthroughs which were the main contributors to pushing down overall jacket cost by almost £6 million.

For the jacket installation, the twin cranes onboard the *S7000* would lift the jacket – weighing 6800t with rigging – from the *S44* transportation barge in the horizontal position, rotate this to the vertical and lower it to the seabed using a single crane. To reduce the load on this crane, the four jacket legs would be sealed at their ends by diaphragms to provide buoyancy as the structure enters the water. Traditional 'good practice' in such operations considers the risk of damage to a

Jacket, template and piles Key areas of savings achieved by the alliance	Single computer model for design and fabrication drawings
Streamlined jacket design reduced steel by 690t	Low preheat welding
Piles reduced from 16 to 12	Reduced inspection and documentation
Elimination of multiple leg compartments	Combined load out and transportation supports
Simplified mudmats	Trailer load out
Combined riser caisson	Reuse of lifting aids and hydraulic controls
Use of existing pile steel for jacket foundations	Template design simplified
Materials delivered without double handling	Use of existing piles for template installation

diaphragm or other system which would allow flooding of a leg and potentially cause crane overload.

'To meet the conditions of single leg compartment damage requires a limit on the inflow of water into the legs,' explains Brown & Root naval architect Richard French. 'The usual approach is to fabricate watertight bulkheads as subdivisions inside the legs to create smaller contained volumes. These sections must then be fitted with hydraulically actuated valves to permit controlled ballasting as the jacket is installed. The hydraulic control lines, plus the pile grouting pipework, are normally run outside the legs to avoid penetrating the bulkheads, and these lines must also be protected in caissons. Furthermore, all such external systems have to be removed after installation to reduce drag during the platform's service life. The net effect is a significant increase in fabrication and offshore installation costs.'

A challenge to this practice was initiated by BARMAC, leading the team to conduct a detailed risk study into the possibility of eliminating the bulkheads and running all systems inside the jacket legs. This in turn would minimise associated hydraulic systems, ballast valves and component parts, further reducing possibilities of failure. The outcome of the study, again with input from Noble Denton, demonstrated that internal systems would have greater protection from damage and on balance would provide a safer operation. A full safety assessment verified the findings, which offered a reduction of 80t in steelwork and equipment weight. By adopting the new approach savings of £700,000 were added to the gainshare.

'Jacket designers working in isolation would almost certainly not have pursued this idea,' Bill Ebdon comments. 'Co-operation between the alliance members made innovation possible.'

Soon after, a second and even more substantial saving was achieved by the Andrew design team. Channelled through the project's OFI programme, Brown & Root's engineers proposed the number of jacket leg skirt piles – grouped in four clusters of four – could be reduced from sixteen to fourteen, while maintaining pile penetration into the seabed of 96m. By further evaluation of prevailing

Jacket, template and piles
Design

Simplified design of template pile sleeves
decreased fabrication work during
construction of the six-slot drilling
template at Nigg.

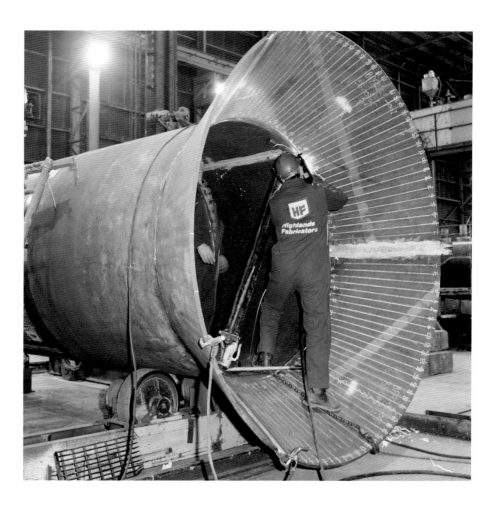

environmental conditions, supported by pile driving records for the region held
by Saipem and Lloyd's Register, it was agreed that an arrangement incorporating
two clusters of three piles and two of four would be sufficient to secure the four
jacket legs.

Eliminating two piles presented the chance to cut fabrication and installation
costs by over £1.5 million. But rather than rest on its laurels, the team was
now fired by the power of success and drove towards removing two more piles.

'It was a challenge we undertook together,' recalls David Cummergen, who
headed Lloyd's Register's certifying team for Andrew. 'The proposal to use only
twelve piles and drive them to 100m to obtain the necessary load bearing capacity
required us to perform a special drivability study to prove the seabed would
respond correctly. Other work was also needed to demonstrate that the
underwater piling hammers would function with the longer piles. By extending
and strengthening the piles the desired result was achieved.'

Andrew's twelve piles, each 120m long, 2.43m in diameter and weighing 500t,
are among the largest in the North Sea. Dispensing with four piles cut jacket
weight by 300t and new pile steel by 1960t. Added savings came with the
decision to re-use 2150t of pile steel already owned by BP, previously fabricated

in Azerbaijan. The exercise of challenging conventional pile design guidelines resulted in total savings to the project of £3.2 million.

Calling traditional practice into question also played a part in influencing the design of Andrew's six-slot drilling template. Following further commercial evaluation soon after project sanction, fabrication of the template had been awarded to BARMAC along with jacket piles in April 1994. The fabricator challenged extensive use of stiffeners in Brown & Root's design of the template pile guides, leading to design simplification and decreased construction work. Saipem's preferred method for installing the template – which involved no diving support, employing instead a lifting frame equipped with underwater hydraulics for its retrieval without diver intervention – was also incorporated into the design. Further gains came by acquiring three unused piles from another North Sea operator, thereafter adding 5m to their length to suit Andrew's template foundations. Combined savings amounted to £400,000.

Design of the template acted as a forerunner for the jacket, helping to establish the alliance's system of sharing and minimising design and fabrication effort. Saipem's installation of the template was scheduled for April 1995, but availability of the *S7000* and the push to begin Andrew's template drilling as soon as possible, called for delivery of the 130t structure a month earlier.

'BARMAC accelerated fabrication enabling us to install the template as the first job of the season in March,' records Saipem alliance manager Tony Press. 'Responding positively to requests of this nature between contractors is by no means normal in the industry – it was a clear display of everyone being aware of the bigger picture on Andrew.'

The mood of co-operation cascaded through the integrated team, instilling confidence that the alliance was truly pulling together as a single force.

'The successes and major gains we were experiencing confirmed that the alliance could really deliver on its promises to reduce Andrew's target costs, which by now stood at £320 million,' says Archie Carmichael. 'As a mark of commitment to the project, BARMAC offered to relax its contractual terms by converting elements of the work which were originally fixed in price to reimbursable at cost. As the workscope was reducing, this provided a saving in expenditure, thus increasing the gainshare for all. In parallel with the jacket, template and piles being optimised, we continuously reviewed our stretched targets, ultimately aiming at £9 million below sanction cost.'

Template installation by *S7000* in March 1995

Jacket, template and piles
Fabrication

Fabrication

> 'It was the first time we were given insight into the whole job – everything was laid out, costs and all, for everyone to see'

Gordon Penman
Project engineer BARMAC

Construction of the Andrew jacket began at the Nigg fabrication yard in northeast Scotland in December 1994. True to its pledge to exclude wasteful man-for-man marking from the project, BP did not establish the conventional client team at site to double check on procedures and progress. Throughout the 16-month construction period the BARMAC fabrication team was responsible for its own performance with no permanent client representative present. At the outturn of the job, productivity for building the Andrew jacket was to surpass even the already impressive levels achieved at the yard on previous projects.

'The 25-strong site project team had been coached in Andrew's alliance philosophy and had actively cascaded that awareness throughout the workforce,' states Gordon Penman. 'It was the first time we were given insight into the whole job – everything was laid out, costs and all, for everyone to see. This reinforced the sense of responsibility for Andrew and helped people feel they were contributing to its success. There was no hesitation in coming forward with new ideas.'

During the early stages of the project, the task of buying jacket steel had passed within the alliance from Brown & Root to BARMAC on the grounds that procurement costs could be reduced. The fabricator established a tripartite agreement with manufacturer British Steel and steel supplier Murray International Metals which enabled some 12,000t of materials to be called directly from the suppliers stocks at Newbridge to the appropriate assembly shop at the yard as required, akin to 'just in time' working practice.

The move proved extremely cost effective by avoiding the stocking and double handling of steel at the fabrication yard and also in halving material wastage by precise ordering. 'The alliance permitted this approach because we had time to think rather than just act under pressure,' says Carmichael. 'Compared with the original cost estimate for steel, we have saved around £1 million.'

Andrew's relatively unpressured schedule proved of benefit to fabrication in other ways, as Richard Wegener, Brown & Root's design liaison engineer within the site team, explains. 'By the time construction began, jacket design had reached a more advanced stage of detail than normally achieved. Designer and fabricator had developed material specifications together, fabrication shop drawings were produced directly from the computer model, and the overall design was inherently more fabricator friendly. The direct result of this was a tenfold reduction in the number of queries arising at site. Those problems which did occur were settled on the spot rather than generating a lengthy exchange of correspondence – a faster response meant less hold up for the workforce and a co-operative working atmosphere.'

Delegation of responsibility to the workforce was already an accepted part of Nigg's working culture, stemming from the quality improvement programme instituted some years before by Brown & Root Highlands Fabricators. Although the merger of the Nigg yard with long-time rival McDermott at Ardersier to form the BARMAC business unit occurred only two months into jacket fabrication, causing understandable disruption, the Nigg workforce remained committed to Andrew's success.

Several aspects of Nigg's working practice fitted well with Andrew's project goals, among them the reduction of inspection and associated documentation. Operating in core teams of welders and fabricators, the workers and supervisors carried out their own quality assurance rather than stop at each stage of a job to have it formally inspected, a process which entailed unwanted downtime and generated unnecessary paperwork, says welding supervisor Colin Thompson.

'It used to be that a welder would produce a root weld and would then have to wait for it to be checked and accepted in succession by foreman, quality control and client before he could complete it. This would always mean waiting. But now the welder and supervisor decide together if it's good or not – this is our responsibility. Doing away with the extra interfaces that do not really contribute to the result has made the job run much more smoothly.'

Quality assurance manager Jack Marshall is quick to praise the success of self-inspection. 'Response was good from the start, but it soon became a matter of pride – no-one wanted to be the first to have a weld repaired. As a result, all 94 closure butt welds on the jacket – performed outdoors at high level – have proved fault free when checked by non-destructive testing (NDT). This is a remarkable achievement, a first for any yard.'

'Receiving materials and drawings on time made a big difference to efficiency as we didn't have to work out of sequence'

Lachie Winton
Fabricator BARMAC

The alliance in action

Jacket, template and piles
Fabrication

'We were trusted to carry out our own quality control without unnecessary client interference'

Jimmy Sutherland
Fabricator BARMAC

Jacket foundation piles were fabricated by BARMAC at Ardersier.

A major element promoting such success has been co-operation within the core teams and through consultation with the workforce. 'We were invited by the project manager to give our views on the best way to go about the work,' says section manager Sanders More. 'This enabled us to put forward possibilities we've always been aware of, including reducing material wastage, adopting more productive shift patterns and successfully challenging the need for full NDT on temporary attachments. In one afternoon session alone we identified major savings for the project.'

Appreciation of the chance to contribute ideas is echoed by fabrication supervisor Donnie Campbell. 'For the pile sleeve clusters we proposed that the shear plates could be cut to the theoretical size rather than oversize as was always done for years, which involved a great deal of corrective work. We had the confidence in our abilities to do this and were permitted to prove it, saving 120 manhours in burning one shear plate alone. Efficiency in building the pile clusters was twenty percent up on previous jobs.'

Co-operation during fabrication also extended beyond the Nigg yard to the alliance. Polypropylene coating of the 10in diameter oil export riser pipe,

fabricated by BARMAC, was performed more cost effectively by adding it to Allseas' larger coating contract for the subsea lines; some large steel tubulars for the integrated deck structure were rolled at cost by BARMAC on behalf of TJB; and clearing seafastenings from Saipem's *S44* transportation barge, remaining from the vessel's previous assignment, was carried out by BARMAC to avoid possible delays in loadout.

Andrew's jacket piles were the focus of further co-operation. BP had available some 2150t of certified piles, fabricated in Baku, Azerbaijan for the company's Unity platform which were never used. These were purchased by the alliance, and although BARMAC had costs in its contract to cover the transport of the piles, a subcontract involving Dutch and British contractors proved a cheaper option, contributing £60,000 to the gainshare. Fabrication of Andrew's twelve piles, involving over 6000t of steel, was undertaken at Ardersier by BARMAC, along with rolling of heavy walled tubulars over 70mm thick.

Jacket frame roll-up (top) and pile cluster erection.

Welding techniques also benefited from alliance input. 'Trials previously carried out by TJB suggested there was scope to reduce the degree of preheating traditionally employed in welding operations,' says Brown & Root's lead materials engineer Doug Stannard. 'The normalised, quenched and tempered steels supplied by British Steel today are of very high quality and require less preheat to drive out impurities before welding begins. The net result is a significant saving in preparation time and more comfortable working conditions.'

Low preheat was used for all manual and semi-automatic welds on the jacket, replacing time-consuming electrical heating to temperatures up to 150°C with gas heating to less than 50°C. The consequent improvement in working conditions was appreciated by the workforce, as welder Donnie Leonard points out. 'High temperatures meant you were continuously having to step back from the workface. But on Andrew the environment was far easier to work in - if a welder is more comfortable, he's also more productive.'

The yard's successful track record in fabricating critical structural elements formed the basis for another challenge to accepted practice. Pipeline risers are normally subjected to a 24-hour pressure test to detect leaks before being installed in protective caissons, and a repeat test thereafter. But in twenty years, no leaks had occurred in risers fabricated at Nigg, giving the team the confidence to propose that all risers – numbering six, plus one J-tube – be installed in a single sealed 1.2m diameter caisson attached to the jacket, and hydrotested for six hours to demonstrate structural integrity. Once the risers were connected offshore, they would receive the full 24-hour strength test to gain acceptance from the Health & Safety Executive, the net result providing significant savings to the project.

Maximising indoor work for the jacket was planned from the outset. The advanced state of jacket design – including installation attachments required by

Jacket, template and piles
Fabrication

'We were always waiting for the inevitable design change, but it never came'

Sanders More
Section manager BARMAC

Saipem – plus timely delivery of materials and equipment, enabled the vast bulk of appurtenances to be attached under cover in Nigg's assembly halls before the jacket frames were rolled up in October 1995. Typifying the degree of completion were the jacket's protective anodes: of 404 anodes all but two were attached indoors. 'Productivity levels in the assembly halls exceeded expectations, cutting manhours from an expected 110,000 to 69,000,' notes senior production engineer Jimmy McIntosh.

Construction manager Peter Mackay attributes this success to a combination of two factors. 'The work was planned to push hard in the prefabrication phase so that in the subsequent more costly assembly stage we would be ahead, and therefore able to work single shift manhours. But there was more involved than just detailed planning – this had to be put into practice. The core teams at Nigg have been fine-tuned over many projects and the quality improvement programme has assisted this, but the sense of trust and ownership on Andrew really enabled them to deliver. We were given our freedom; in return we gave our commitment to the project's success. I believe the alliance has received a better quality product without a client representative on site.'

Several weeks before jacket loadout on 7 April 1996, the structure was substantially complete, dispensing with the common routine of carrying over activities to be finished onboard the transportation barge at the quayside. A detailed dimensional survey showed the entire structure to be well within specification tolerances, underlining the fact that self-regulating quality control by the workforce, backed up by periodic audits, had achieved a result at least equal to that of traditional inspection procedures.

But it is in summing all such achievements during construction that the overall impact of the alliance on jacket fabrication is best realised. Workforce productivity outstripped the high performance levels laid down for Andrew, as project controls engineer Steve Conway describes. 'For the sanction estimate we based our expected productivity on the most recent jacket we had built, which itself had come in almost ten percent better than target. Andrew has pushed this still further, improving by almost another ten percent, including work on the template and piles. Given that the project was carried out against an unsettling backdrop of two large construction companies merging, the final result is a tribute to the BARMAC workforce.'

At project sanction, estimated manhours for jacket fabrication alone were put at some 580,000. With major design changes reducing the number of piles and removing internal leg compartments, the workscope soon reduced to around 500,000. But by 'smarter working' at Nigg, further motivated by the co-operative atmosphere encouraged by the alliance, Andrew's jacket was built for less than 440,000 manhours.

'When the job started all indications were that the jacket would be produced at around 78 manhours per tonne,' observes Mike Connolly, who joined the

Trailers were used to loadout the jacket onto the transportation barge *S44* in April 1996

BARMAC team as project manager in the middle of construction. 'The final outcome is around 66 manhours per tonne, beating anything we've achieved before for a jacket of this size. The bottom line is that we've surpassed the stretched target of £25 million set in 1994 for jacket, template and piles.'

Fabrication and materials costs for the three components totalled £24 million. The resulting £9 million saving delivered to the Andrew gainshare is due in almost equal measure to reduction in fabrication workscope – arising from early challenges within the alliance during design – and improved performance across all aspects of construction. 'You couldn't ask for a more positive demonstration of what can be achieved when you're freed from the burdens of the past,' concludes Archie Carmichael.

Fabrication cost summary (£ thousands)
Jacket, template and piles

	Jacket	Template & piles	Total
Sanction estimate	£26,360	£6,643	£33,003
Final cost	£19,673	£4,327	£24,000
Savings to gainshare	£ 4,687	£2,316	£ 9,003

'We're proud of our work on every job but there was something extra on Andrew, an extra degree of trust'

James 'Darkie' Watson
Welder BARMAC

Jacket, template and piles
Fabrication

'You couldn't ask for a more positive demonstration of what can be achieved when you're freed from the burdens of the past'

Archie Carmichael
Alliance project manager BARMAC

Jacket, template and piles
Installation

Installation

Jacket lifted, in place on seabed, and
piling operations beginning.

On 29 April 1996, the Andrew jacket set sail from Nigg on its two day voyage
to the field. Weighing 7535t with rigging and seafastenings, the completed
structure made the 230km journey onboard Saipem's *S44* transportation barge.
With a deck area measuring 190m long by 50m wide, *S44* ranks among the largest
transportation barges, accommodating the 134m by 45m jacket without the need
for supporting steelwork overhanging the sides of the barge, and enabling Saipem
and BARMAC to combine loadout and transportation grillage with a net reduction
of 300t of steel.

The twelve foundation piles for the jacket had departed Ardersier onboard *S42*
a week earlier bound for Stavanger, where they were transferred onto the deck of
S7000. On 1 May, jacket and piles made their rendezvous in the Andrew field.

Installation of the jacket by semisubmersible *S7000* – the largest and most
sophisticated heavy lift vessel in the world – was carried out with the vessel held
on station using its own dynamic positioning (DP) system rather than the more
frequently employed anchor mooring system.

'Eliminating the spread of anchors removes the risk of damage to jacket, anchor
lines and the subsea pipelines and equipment already installed in the field,' explains
Saipem project engineer Mark Kilcran. 'The operation is a sensitive one and is
somewhat unusual given the combination of jacket size, template docking and
dynamic positioning.'

One factor influencing that sensitivity was prevailing weather, which delayed
the installation by six days following the decision of Saipem's vessel superintendent,
responsible for the offshore operation. But in the afternoon of 7 May, with
conditions now judged to be safe, installation began.

At 1500 hours the twin giant cranes of *S7000* – held on station by the vessel's
12 thrusters – lifted the jacket horizontally from the transportation barge. With
the barge towed clear, the jacket was lowered to the water, partially submerging
the structure to gain buoyancy as it was righted to the vertical. At this stage, five
hours into the operation, the lower spreader bar was hydraulically released from its
underwater position, leaving the jacket suspended from the starboard crane only.
Aided by the jacket's buoyancy, static hook load was now in the region of 2500t,
well within the crane's 7000t capacity.

Careful planning and control had been required throughout the lift as Andrew's
jacket dimensions limited clearance between hooks and crane booms to between
2m and 5m. With the vessel operating under DP, the jacket was positioned above
the preinstalled drilling template on the seabed 115m below water level. As the
structure was lowered, ballasting of the jacket was required. This operation was
hampered by malfunction of one of the jacket's hydraulically actuated flooding

valves, corrected in due course using the backup systems for underwater intervention by remotely operated vehicle deployed from *S7000*.

Precise positioning of the jacket was achieved by two docking piles located at the template. As the structure approached the template it first contacted the 2m diameter primary docking pile standing some 12m above the seabed, and was then manoeuvred to locate the secondary docking pile. At 0345 hours on 8 May the jacket's four mudmats touched down on the seafloor.

In turn, each of the twelve 120m long foundation piles was now lifted from the deck and stabbed into the jacket pile sleeves, securing the 6100t structure. Pile driving, using a Menck MHU1700 underwater hammer, began at 0930 hours on 9 May, completing the operation 36 hours later as each 2.43m pile penetrated 100m into the seabed. Grouting of the piles followed. By 13 May, Lloyd's Register confirmed the Andrew jacket installation to be safely completed and ready to accept the platform's integrated deck.

Saipem's *S7000* crane vessel, with foundation piles onboard, lifting the Andrew jacket prior to upending.

Topsides

'We have seen
construction manhours
almost double on
some jobs without
adding any value to
the project'

Alex Dawson
Alliance board member TJB

With Andrew's topsides facilities accounting for over half of the project's total cost, the alliance was in no doubt that overall commercial success would be largely dictated by delivering the topsides within the tight budgets set at sanction. Building and equipping the platform's process-utilities deck, drilling module and living quarters was targeted at £150 million, on top of which came the costs of design, installation, offshore hookup and commissioning, pushing the bottom line beyond £200 million.

The team had good cause for concern. North Sea developments had a history of cost overruns attributable to topsides facilities seemingly veering out of control, particularly in the later stages of a project as a vast array of equipment and materials are brought together to form complex operating systems. The unallocated provision normally added to development budgets had been regularly consumed by unpredictable – though not entirely unexpected – extra costs mounting towards the tail end of the job.

'Most offshore projects have suffered to some degree from growth in manhours during the construction stage,' comments alliance board member Alex Dawson, managing director of TJB's Port Clarence fabrication yard. 'The topsides is effectively at the end of the production line and is subject to a whole catalogue of influences. We have seen construction manhours almost double on some jobs without adding any value to the project, resulting in the propagation of a culture of blame and contractual conflict. The project is then seriously penalised again by the carryover of unfinished work, dramatically escalating the cost of offshore completion.'

Two of the primary causes of such negative impacts are well recognised by the wider industry. Late deliveries of equipment packages and materials to the fabrication site routinely force inefficient rescheduling and delay work progress, while packages only partially completed also have severe consequences for onshore commissioning programmes. Perhaps even more notorious for knocking fabrication plans off course are the arrival of late design changes, attributable to poor design definition, lack of understanding and communication between contractors, or the untimely intervention of the client's operations team.

'We knew that if we could sort out the interface between topsides designer and fabricator we could make an immediate impact on the root causes of these problems,' adds TJB alliance project manager Brian Colpitts. 'The alliance presented us with the opportunity to pursue this, to integrate the design and build programme and exert control over unnecessary changes.'

Uniting Andrew's topsides designers and fabricators was to prove of unimagined benefit over the months of co-operative effort which followed, ultimately achieving the primary goal of preventing large-scale fabrication growth and cost overruns. The liberty to work together without adversity resulted in greater efficiency in the construction stage, supported from the outset by a fundamentally new approach to equipment procurement, and in the later stages of the project, achieved an industry benchmark in onshore commissioning and completion. When the fully operational integrated deck headed from the River Tees for the open sea on schedule in May 1996, only seven record-setting weeks remained before first oil flowed from the Andrew field.

'We knew that if we could sort out the interface between topsides designer and fabricator we could make an immediate impact'

Brian Colpitts
Alliance project manager TJB

Deck design

Detailed design of Andrew's topsides began in earnest in early 1994 following sanction award. Having already experienced the benefits of open co-operation in producing the sanction estimate, the alliance was determined not to go the way of many previous projects in rigidly marking out individual contractor's territories. The London-based team pooled the skills of managers, engineers and designers from the alliance companies to develop the integrated deck design, ensuring that decisions were taken not on the usual basis of satisfying single interests, but on the broader front of identifying methods – be they for design, fabrication, installation or operation – which would inject best value into the project.

'Added confidence was given to the team by the fact that the project's Statement of Requirements (SOR) had been effectively frozen at sanction,' recounts BP's Mike Brown, topsides co-ordinator and BRO for the deck. 'It's not uncommon for the SOR to undergo changes as a project proceeds, which naturally has a major impact on design and fabrication. For Andrew we had high level assurance through the maturity of the SOR that this would not happen.'

Fundamental to Andrew's topsides facilities was the commitment to an integrated deck, weighing around 9,900t in total, which could be substantially commissioned onshore and installed in a single lift offshore. The structure consisted of three key elements: a three-level process and utilities deck, incorporating a 24-slot wellbay, to be fabricated by TJB in Teesside; an 1850t drilling module to be designed and built under an engineer-procure-construct (EPC) contract by Santa Fe; while under another EPC contract, Emtunga of Sweden would deliver the platform's 72-bed accommodation module, weighing 520t.

Capable of exporting 70,000bpd of oil, including 12,000bpd from the Cyrus field, plus around 1 million m³/d of gas, the topsides facilities were designed with a focus on life cycle costs, opting for proven, standard equipment with high reliability and low maintenance.

Topsides
Deck design

Much attention centred on the process-utilities deck, construction of which began within two months of sanction. With design and fabrication moving ahead together, interdependence between Brown & Root and TJB led to an unprecedented degree of co-operation.

'We worked hard to simplify the interfaces between us,' relates Brown & Root's John Gregory, engineering manager for the integrated team. 'The cost targets we had set were extremely challenging and we were keenly aware that new ways of working were absolutely vital to our cause. By having an open dialogue with the fabricators we discovered what they really needed from us as designers, rather than what we had always presumed they would want. It sounds simple now, but at the time this was a big step forward in eliminating old prejudices.'

Co-operation between the two was highlighted in the area of producing design and construction drawings, activities which frequently share a troubled interface involving much duplication of effort to create final drawings for the fabrication shops. Using its enhanced 3D CAD techniques, Brown & Root produced detailed models of the topsides structure and all facilities to act as a single database at design office and fabrication site, with TJB specifying the style and content of drawings needed to support construction. Drawings and schedules – including those for cutting plates, rolling tubulars, and fabricating pipe spools – were generated directly from the Triton and proprietary PDMS software models and transferred electronically to site, dispensing with rework in Teesside.

'The effect was remarkable,' emphasises Gregory. 'While we expended some 35,000 extra manhours in the design office, more than 100,000 hours were eliminated at site compared to original expectations.'

'Early input helped improve several design aspects which made the whole deck more fabrication friendly'

Dave Cram
Construction manager TJB

Direct input from TJB's engineers determined the most logical sequence for constructing the deck, based on the 'pancake' method of fabricating each of the three deck levels separately, followed by vertical stacking. 'Early input helped improve several design aspects which made the whole deck more fabrication friendly,' observes TJB construction manager Dave Cram. 'For primary steel we simplified joint and stiffening designs, cut down the number of cast nodes, and reduced the amount of welding needed to fabricate plate girders by ordering the largest steel plate available instead of joining together several smaller sections. Working with Brown & Root's metallurgists we also adopted lower preheat welding methods based on our in-house trials, which not only made savings for the deck but were also used to good effect on the jacket at Nigg.'

Simplifying plate girder manufacturing techniques led to a decrease of 200,000 manhours in primary steel fabrication, contributing positively to the project's safety record in the process.

Installation of the deck was another primary influence on the design of the structure. The massive rigging used for offshore lifts – in Andrew's case weighing

200t – requires purpose-made attachments built into the deck and extensive temporary steelwork to support the rigging during transportation.

'Positioning of lifting aids frequently clashes with major items of topsides equipment which must consequently be left off during deck construction, to be installed and commissioned offshore,' states Ian Harrison, lead structural design engineer. 'On top of this is the cost of providing and removing temporary steelwork and rigging. Together with Saipem we devised alternative ways to avoid most of these tasks.'

Rather than manufacture four new lifting point castings, Saipem provided existing castings from a previous deck installation, tested and recertified, to save the project over £300,000. The attachments were raised above the top level of the deck by locating them on 15m tall columns, leaving the weather deck free for the installation of Andrew's main power generators. Lift rigging was secured on the platform's helideck and within the drilling pipe rack, dispensing with additional steel laydown areas. 'Hundred's of tonnes of temporary steelwork were eliminated,' adds Harrison.

With the goal of achieving a minimum facilities platform, Andrew's process and utilities areas are relatively conventional in design. Single train processing includes two-stage separation, gas dehydration, two-stage compression and gas reinjection, metering and export. Three gas turbine generators provide up to 18MW of power, while twin main oil line pumps export the field's crude to the Forties pipeline system.

The three power generators provide 130% of peak electrical load and a more cost effective solution over the life of the field than two larger units as power demand will decrease in later years of operation; an integrated system for electrical distribution and switchgear reduces power transformers from three to two. One notable innovation is the complete integration of process control and monitoring, emergency shutdown, and fire and gas detection systems. Instead of three separate systems, those on Andrew are combined into a single system – an offshore first – removing design, installation and maintenance interfaces between different suppliers, reducing procurement effort, and yielding savings in hardware.

Ideas for attaining best value for Andrew came forward from all engineering disciplines, stimulated by a 'right to challenge' ethos. 'We were given freedom to express ourselves from the top,' comments lead architectural engineer Rob Skivington. 'The atmosphere of co-operation was not only between alliance companies, but internally too – it helped reduce the traditional interdisciplinary rivalry that exists on projects and generated a more effective team-solving approach.'

Piping systems, which bear a reputation for proving problematic across the design-fabricator interface, often causing rework and cost escalation at site, were a principal beneficiary of the integrated working relationship developing for Andrew.

Topsides
Deck design

'The analysis for Andrew revealed that topsides commissioning had to start much earlier – eight months before loadout – and overlap fabrication'

Mike Brown
Topsides co-ordinator BP

Topsides
Deck design

Computer aided design provided a link between design and fabrication activities.

'Drawings were issued for construction only when we were confident they would not be subjected to change later,' explains Brown & Root project engineer George Morris. 'On other projects drawings would go out purely to meet the contractual milestone dates, even if they were not yet needed at site, and frequently had to be changed after fabrication had started. On this job we learned to wait – it wasn't easy, but it paid off.'

TJB's piping engineers worked alongside Brown & Root to determine the true need dates at site, prioritising pipework to match the build sequence and providing more time to progress and confirm design details. CAD played an important role throughout the piping operation, linking design and fabrication activities. From the 3D CAD model of the integrated deck, piping isometric drawings – the basis for fabricating pipework – were generated entirely automatically without manual enhancement for direct delivery to the shop floor, the result of new software developments in use for the first time. Input from TJB determined the preferred pipe spool sizes to assist efficient manufacture and installation, and pipe support details were added only when required.

'Performing as a team from the outset brought tremendous advantages,' adds Glenn Helyer, TJB's piping co-ordinator. 'The most visible effect of producing complete piping fabrication drawings from the model was to cut some 40,000 manhours of drawing office effort in Teesside. But there were other benefits too. Expensive rework of fabricated pipelines was avoided, and site queries were also minimised. You might expect up to 10,000 queries on a job this size all of which would have to be documented and await slow answers; on Andrew only 500 occurred and were resolved in days, which prevented disruption to the erection programme.'

The net effect of having materials and completed drawings available when required achieved a quantum leap in piping productivity at site. With TJB installing 600t of pipework fabricated by sister company Redpath Engineering Services (RES), all piping systems were completed within 370,000 manhours with productivity over 90%. 'In the past you might have been looking at twice these manhours and only half the productivity,' reflects Helyer.

'The CAD model produced the best clash-free design we've ever used; it was very rare to find a clash'

Glenn Morley
Piping engineer TJB

In line with the project's goal of reducing documentation, inspection and expediting, design engineers undertook a more proactive role in the interface with equipment package suppliers. Prescriptive specifications from BP and Brown & Root for equipment and material packages were put to one side, issuing instead functional specifications inviting suppliers to offer standard products.

'Responsibility for selecting package suppliers and related technical decisions passed to us on this job,' comments lead telecommunications engineer Roland Hawes. 'Rigid client specifications and preferred suppliers were not imposed and innovation was encouraged. This was an improvement in many ways: it allowed us to dispense with the usual 'North Sea extras' and meant that for fast moving technologies, such as telecoms, we could pursue cost saving solutions proposed by suppliers. As just one of many examples, this flexibility enabled telecoms cabling to be reduced by twenty percent.'

Supplier selection was approached differently for Andrew. Normal technical and commercial criteria were joined by less tangible yet equally important considerations – typically a supplier's commitment and control – all of which were weighted in evaluating tenders. 'Best value does not necessarily mean the lowest price,' points out instruments package engineer Peter Ramsdale.

Superior supplier performance was identified as one of the key elements vital to the success of Andrew's ambitious plan for onshore completion. Minimising offshore work by maximising onshore commissioning of the topsides facilities is a logical goal all projects set, but rarely – if ever – achieve to the degree envisaged. As problems build up during fabrication due to late deliveries and conflicting priorities, projects fall into the conventional trap of leaving an increasing backlog to be solved offshore, usually by another contractor. 'Many projects, which claim to be '99% complete' when the topsides sail away, face major offshore work programmes in reality,' asserts topsides co-ordinator Mike Brown.

'From even before Andrew's sanction we were developing a commissioning plan that concentrated on the designing-out of offshore work. By tracking back from

Topsides
Deck design

the planned loadout date in April 1996, an accurate sequence was established for the arrival of design deliverables and equipment at site which would permit commissioning to be accomplished onshore. Historically projects tend to try to complete the outfitting of topsides modules before beginning commissioning, attempting to squeeze this into an inadequate three months at the end of the job. The analysis for Andrew revealed that commissioning had to start much earlier – eight months before loadout – and needed to overlap fabrication.'

Commissioning became the driving force behind the project's overall planning schedule, determining realistic delivery dates and prioritising design activities. In the months after sanction the profile of onshore commissioning was steadily raised to become a dominant activity directly influencing Andrew's potential success.

BP's operations team, which was to play a central role in the commissioning phase, was also actively contributing to Andrew's topsides design and fabrication.

'Joining Andrew at sanction was the earliest an OIM had taken part in a BP project,' declares Owen Chappell, one of Andrew's two offshore installation managers. 'It provided the opportunity to have input not only to operations issues, but to the overall outcome of the project, to be involved in the front end decision process rather than the usual 'stand-off' approach.'

The approach he refers to stems from the perception that operations teams join a project late in the day and indulge in 'preferential engineering', causing change and disruption. For Andrew the operations team was selected on a markedly

---

Topsides design and fabrication
Key contributions to savings

Early input to design from fabricator and operations team

Structural details simplified to produce 'fabricator friendly' design

Detailed construction drawings produced by design team and transferred electronically to site

Cast structural nodes replaced by fabricated nodes

Low preheat welding

Combined electrical and instrument equipment supports

Reduced inspection and documentation

Construction schedule driven by commissioning programme

Realistic fabrication need dates determined delivery of drawings, equipment and materials to site

Improved communications via open plan completions centres in London and Teesside

Early delivery of drilling and accommodation modules

Integrated construction and operations team for commissioning

different basis from that normally employed, focusing strongly on attitudes which would support the facilities project and performance of the asset, rather than take a more limited operations-oriented view. 'We didn't join the project to find fault,' adds operations engineer Derek McCusker, 'we came to learn how to accommodate what had already been done and how best to operate the platform.'

Those changes which were proposed by operations were subjected to a rigorous justification process whereby change was adopted only if improved safety or significant added value resulted – 'nice to haves' were strictly rejected. A case in point where operations input was applied to good advantage centred on the platform's main oil line export pumps. The team presented a detailed study demonstrating that under certain conditions water content in the oil could upset pump operation, leading to process shutdowns and potential lost oil production valued at up to £1.6 million per year. Although the solution required major redesign to pumps and associated pipework, and delayed equipment delivery to site, the added capital expenditure incurred was deemed to be entirely justified when compared with the recurrent savings in operating costs.

Deck fabrication

Within Andrew's target cost at sanction TJB's estimate for building the integrated deck totalled £53.8 million, incorporating 1.4 million manhours to fabricate the process-utilities deck, install the drilling and accommodation modules, and commission the topsides. Manhours were reimbursed at cost along with other items including provision of some materials, while overheads and profit were fixed.

'This price was a true stretched target,' recalls Brian Colpitts, TJB alliance manager. 'Through co-operation in the integrated team prior to sanction we had already driven out many of the normal costs we expect to incur. Decks of this size and complexity have historically taken over 250 manhours per tonne to build – we were targeting some thirty percent below this, including work on the other module interfaces and a major onshore commissioning programme. From past trends the figure of 1.4 million manhours could readily have grown to 2 million or more. The challenge was to prevent that happening on Andrew.'

Early steel deliveries to TJB's Port Clarence yard, purchased from British Steel under an existing BP master agreement, saw deck fabrication get away to a timely start at the end of March 1994. The process-utilities deck was constructed in four primary sections; 75m long by 36m wide intermediate and cellar decks were fabricated in parallel in two adjacent assembly halls; the weather deck was built outside under temporary protection; while in another hall, a smaller structural subassembly was constructed which would contain the platform's temporary refuge and support the accommodation module. The reliable arrival of materials on site

Topsides
Deck fabrication

'For the first time all working construction drawings went directly from designer to fabrication shops'

John Noble
Services manager TJB

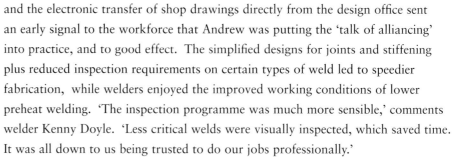

and the electronic transfer of shop drawings directly from the design office sent an early signal to the workforce that Andrew was putting the 'talk of alliancing' into practice, and to good effect. The simplified designs for joints and stiffening plus reduced inspection requirements on certain types of weld led to speedier fabrication, while welders enjoyed the improved working conditions of lower preheat welding. 'The inspection programme was much more sensible,' comments welder Kenny Doyle. 'Less critical welds were visually inspected, which saved time. It was all down to us being trusted to do our jobs professionally.'

With plate girder manufacture accomplished, assembly of the decks commenced in July. The positive impact of suppliers' packages being delivered as planned, soon began to be felt as outfitting of the decks followed on without delay, installing large items of process equipment including separators, heat exchangers and other vessels. 'Equipment delivery was a major improvement over traditional practice,' says Colpitts. 'With the exception of the main oil pumps which were undergoing a design change, all large items arrived on time, avoiding the need to leave spaces and perform difficult insertion manoeuvres later. The supplier procurement initiative introduced by BP and Brown & Root paid dividends in this respect.'

In January 1995, the decks – already blasted and painted, with fireproofing installed below – were brought from the halls on trailers and stacked vertically in sequence over a period of three days. 'These were the most complete decks we've ever stacked,' construction manager Dave Cram points out. 'Compared with the planned programme, we had achieved more work than we expected, such that by the end of January with some 289,000 manhours expended, productivity was 103%.'

Working under cover and at lower levels – inherent features of the 'pancake' build method – also brought added safety benefits to the project, explains TJB safety manager Brian Hall. 'With the decks at ground level there is far less need for scaffold towers and ladders to gain access, and generally more space to work in than when building the entire deck as a box. Accidents due to falls, welding and manual handling all decreased on Andrew, cutting the frequency rate by half compared to the previous project in the yard.' Detailed outfitting of the deck ensued, installing further equipment items and the many systems required for their interconnection and control. The topsides commissioning programme, now planned in greater detail and targeted at onshore completion, called for priority to be given to the utilities area of the deck. Remaining large equipment items were also installed on schedule; main generators and gas reinjection compressors in April, the platform's crane in May, and main gas compressors in June.

In the outfitting stage of large topsides decks, problems which occur due to late delivery of design details and equipment packages can be exacerbated as the

Intermediate deck leaving fabrication hall prior to stacking.

different workforce disciplines and trades attempt to put their individual schedule requirements ahead of others. Work can often be delayed by unavailability of support services, for example scaffolding or fireproofing; at other times changes affecting one discipline may force completed work of another to be removed and repeated, all of which contributes to unproductive territorial adversity. In Andrew's case the workforce had already experienced at first hand the alliance's good results in the co-ordinated success up to deck stacking, conferring an optimistic outlook that the project would continue to run smoothly. 'An atmosphere of greater co-operation and willingness to help had grown with this job, limiting the frustrations which often lead to disputes between the disciplines,' observes yard manager Brian Jopling. The task now was to ensure the spirit of co-operation continued as the workforce grew towards its 650-strong peak.

Recognising that open communication between the disciplines was vital to keep information and productivity flowing, the project took the simple yet highly effective step of grouping supervisors and construction engineers together, rather than in separate locations around the site.

In the London project office an innovatory completions centre had been designed to act as an information hub to support the construction phase. In parallel at the Port Clarence yard, two completions rooms were set up, providing direct links to the London team, but more importantly acting as the nerve centre for controlling the day-to-day progress of fabrication. Site superintendents, construction engineers and subcontractors, plus engineers

'We were installing pipework within two weeks of stacking Andrew's decks – usually the major vessels haven't even arrived at site by this stage'

Derek Roberts
Construction engineer TJB

73

Topsides
Deck fabrication

Communicating to complete

To support the high activity phases of construction and commissioning in Teesside an information-intensive design environment was created in the project's offices in London. The Andrew 'completions centre' acted as a central information hub, bringing together key individuals from the design disciplines to provide rapid and accurate response to problems and queries arising at the fabrication site.

Conceived and designed by Brown & Root's architects and computer engineers working on the Andrew project, the high-tech completions centre was equipped and laid out to promote effective information flow between engineers in the room and beyond. Covering 195 square metres, the centre houses a direct television link to Teesside, large multi-access computer display screens, electronic messaging board, overhead projectors, a video conference centre, two meeting areas and 20 workstations arranged in four semicircles. Low-heat fibre optic lighting cuts out glare from computer screens, lending a futuristic feel to the environment.

'The facilities enabled speedy checking and review of proposed solutions with face-to-face access to people in Teesside over 300km away,' says lead architectural engineer Rob Skivington. 'With the main information sources displayed in the centre of the room on large screens, a natural openness was encouraged among the team, avoiding the development of individual information preserves which tend to occur on conventional projects.'

Regular daily communication ensured that issues were dealt with quickly, and reinforced the reality of a single extended team working towards a common goal rather than two separate teams working out of rythym. The immediate success of the completions centre gave impetus to the development a few months later of two more open plan completions rooms at the fabrication site, further enhancing communication links throughout the project. With live video images of their counterparts projected into the centres in London and Teesside, designers and fabricators operated in one large 'virtual' centre as members of the same completions team, maintaining the flow of information vital to Andrew's ambitious construction and commissioning programme. The cost of developing the centres was far outweighed by the boost to efficiency injected into Andrew's topsides completion, and the subsequent economic benefits to the project.

Weather deck lifted for stacking.

from the London design disciplines and certifying authority, operated alongside one another as part of the completions team.

'The reason the completions rooms made such a positive impact was simply that people spoke to each other,' comments RES electrical engineer Henry Harris. 'In the open plan environment you got to know what was going on with other disciplines and could more easily avoid trying to work in the same place at the same time. It made for a much better atmosphere between us – the only enemies were the schedule and budget.'

Freed from the burdens of man-for-man marking and continuous deferral to a client representative, decision making from the completions team provided a faster response to the workforce. 'On other projects it could take 14 days to get permission to move even a handrail,' says structural superintendent Alan Little. 'On Andrew we could sort matters out ourselves, or at most with a short phone call.' The doors to the completions rooms were open to all, encouraging helpful feedback from the fabrication workplace, cutting back on formalised written procedures, and generating cross-discipline assistance. 'We didn't have to book days in advance for other services; we received the support we needed without the usual friction and delays,' recounts electrical foreman Dennis Elwick.

'Everyone was entitled to go into the completions centre and raise problems directly. There was no long chain of command to slow things down'

Jeff Robson
Plater TJB

Closer ties extended beyond the alliance companies in the team to the main subcontractors involved in constructing the topsides. Taking the project's gainshare concept a step further, TJB entered into risk and reward agreements with subcontractors Barrier Offshore Engineering for painting and fireproofing, and with G+H McGill for thermal insulation, architectural and HVAC work.

Topsides
Deck fabrication

RES, a sister company to TJB, carried out pipework fabrication plus the installation of electrical and instrumentation systems under TJB's alliance contract.

'Involving subcontractors in gainshare agreements required considerable adjustment to our normal way of thinking,' says RES project manager Alan Weaver. 'There was understandable scepticism at first; supervisors, foremen and fitters all had to become aligned to the idea. Andrew's atmosphere of co-operation helped with this. Now no-one waits for paper instructions, they just get on with the work.' All subcontractors performed as members of the integrated team, introducing more efficient practices to reduce manhours by some 20%, and sharing in the resulting savings under their respective gainshare contracts.

Much of the 'feel good factor' permeating the project could be attributed to the visible progress of the topsides construction, proceeding without widespread disruptions caused by changes in design or unreliable materials delivery. In the early stages of design, the approach taken by the project team was one of positive rather than negative change control, explains engineering manager John Gregory. 'If you attempt to stamp out all change it goes underground and comes back to surprise you later. By openly inviting people to come forward with suggestions and accepting those which contribute to the project, change can be better harnessed as a beneficial force.'

But in the real world problems and changes do occur, regardless of the planned good intentions of project teams. Design changes were relatively limited in extent, largely due to joint input in creating the CAD model, which over the course of the project served as a focus between designers and fabricators for discussion of proposed changes before any action was taken. While design change was controlled, delivery of equipment and materials did in some instances create problems. For the majority of equipment packages, numbering around 130 in total, the project's approach of allowing suppliers to provide fit-for-purpose products yielded the required quality result. Others – perhaps less than 10% – fell short of the mark, causing remedial work at site.

The key to managing the changes rested in open dialogue between the project and suppliers to find an effective solution rather than resort to the traditional response of immediately hitting vendors with contractual claims, thus introducing further delay. Two cases in particular threatened to hamper fabrication progress. When metallurgical faults were discovered in part of a super duplex pipe fittings order sourced in Italy – resulting in dozens of fittings having to be cut out of pipework and replaced – the supplier accepted responsibility without argument, worked with the project to determine the cause and resupplied quickly. Total commitment and speedy response meant no penalties were imposed on the vendor. Faults were also detected in instrument cabling after several kilometres had been installed, again causing stripping out of completed work. The project accepted the

Cellar and intermediate decks stacked with weather deck to follow

Three deck levels in place with outfitting in progress.

faults were of a unique nature which could not have been identified by the normal factory tests, and worked with the manufacturer to solve the problem, developing a modified production process. Within three weeks some 20km of new cable had been produced and delivered, the supplier bearing the extra costs without also attracting further penalties. In each case, historical adversity was replaced by proactive co-operation on the part of the supplier and mature understanding from the project; the driving force was to solve the problem and push on rather than stop to apportion blame.

Throughout 1995 the alliance adhered resolutely to its goal of combating fabrication growth by challenging traditional practice and adopting more efficient working methods arising from the flow of co-operative ideas. In October the accommodation module arrived early from Sweden for installation onto the process-utilities deck, followed two months later by the drilling module from Singapore. By the end of January 1996, outfitting of the topsides was effectively complete and major headway had also been made into commissioning; total expended manhours were approaching 1.3 million. With overall productivity standing at 94%, Andrew's performance was on target to achieve an exceptionally high level of onshore completion.

Topsides
Drilling facilities

Drilling facilities

Centrally located in Andrew's integrated deck, the platform's 1800t drilling facilities module sits above a 24-slot wellbay housed between process and utilities areas. Over the first two years of production, the rig will complete a series of long horizontal wells into the hydrocarbon-bearing zones of the Andrew reservoir, adding to the four predrilled wells, to deliver the field's scheduled exports of 58,000bpd of oil and around 1 million m³/d of gas.

Alliance member Santa Fe was responsible for the total supply of the drilling module under a lump sum EPC contract, valued at £28 million in the sanctioned target cost. But the company's involvement with Andrew extends beyond the facilities alliance, with Santa Fe participating in the predrilling and platform operations alliances – 'a move calculated to improve the project's overall performance,' explains BP project co-ordinator Paul Bibby.

'The traditional route for new platform drilling facilities, followed by BP and most of the industry, had been to select one contractor to design the facilities, another to build, and a third to operate the rig offshore. This produced two interfaces and invariably resulted in changes being made, particularly towards the end of construction and during offshore hookup when the drilling contractor began to state operational preferences. For Andrew we wanted the driller involved with the design of the facilities to avoid costly rework and to improve drilling efficiency when the platform was in operation.'

An extensive selection process, focusing on a combination of experience and behavioural response under the project's Minimum Conditions of Satisfaction criteria, resulted in Santa Fe joining the project as the second alliance contractor in early 1993.

Oliver Hinton, Santa Fe's alliance project manager at that time, reflects on the strategy. 'The inclusion of drilling operations crew in the early stages helps ensure the design basis is user-oriented. All too often we take over as operator of new and expensive drilling facilities, only to find there are many improvements needed. Involvement from the beginning helped develop a sense of certainty and ownership of the design.'

Responding to the challenge of contributing to the Andrew alliance, Santa Fe took the ownership theme a step further during the selection process by proposing to design, procure and build the drilling facilities under a lump sum contract. 'Based on our experience of doing this for mobile drilling units, we felt confident that we could deliver fit-for-purpose platform drilling facilities for Andrew more cost effectively than via the conventional route,' adds Hinton.

The solution put forward for Andrew was a modularised drilling facility centred on landbased technology already adapted for offshore application, which

'All too often we take over as operator of new and expensive drilling facilities, only to find there are many improvements needed'

Oliver Hinton
Alliance project manager Santa Fe

could be delivered in around 18 months. Compared with conventional platform drilling units the design is both compact and lighter, having a dry weight of 1800t against a more typical 2500t. Of critical importance to Andrew's tight economics the modularised rig showed significant cost benefits – a large integrated-style rig commonly found in the North Sea may have cost half as much again.

From May 1993 Santa Fe worked on the design with its main subcontractor. While design was undertaken in London, equipment supply, assembly and testing of the facilities were to be carried out in Canada and the USA. Underlying the design concept is the ability for the entire rig to be broken down into 24 minimodules, enabling the facilities to be removed by platform crane for use elsewhere by BP if required.

The London design team worked in close liaison with BP's drilling specialists to develop a functional specification for the rig, taking a zero-based engineering approach to justify each item against well needs. The fit-for-purpose design includes standard, proven equipment and optimised storage capacity to match four-day resupply; the degree of mechanisation reflects Andrew's planned drilling programme, with manning levels minimised to reduce operating and accommodation costs. One notable equipment feature is the four-piece telescopic 'bootstrap' mast rather than a derrick, which can be erected by the platform's crane.

Based upon the compact design, Santa Fe's lump sum cost was incorporated into the platform's sanction estimate, with the company opting to take a three percent stake in the project's gainshare agreement. 'At the beginning of presanction design we were not keen on participating in the optional gainshare,' states Hinton. 'We were focused on the risk rather than the potential reward, and felt that our lump sum for the drilling module already contained a risk element. At that stage we were still wary of the performance of other contractors and the chance that they might drift into the 'business as usual' approach, generating a rash of change orders which would push the job over the target cost. But when Brown & Root and TJB took larger stakes in the gainshare it became clear that their motivation was to keep costs down. It was a positive sign which influenced us to take part.'

Santa Fe's relationship with the alliance members was to be put to the test soon after Andrew received sanction. In April 1994, circumstances associated with a major Norwegian offshore project were bringing the financial security of Santa Fe's main subcontractor into question, leading to the conclusion that to proceed with this arrangement for Andrew's drilling facilities would entail an increasing risk to the alliance. The problem was put to the Andrew alliance board along with the proposal that an alternative subcontractor should be brought onboard to complete the work, although costs could increase as a result.

Modularised drilling facilities adapted from landbased designs saved weight and space.

Topsides
Drilling facilities

'By now the alliance
was robust enough to
shoulder the problems
of the participants'

John Jerzak
Drilling facilities BRO BP

'The alliance board was initially concerned by the news,' reports BP's John Jerzak, who as BRO for Andrew's drilling and accommodation modules was responsible for monitoring the interfaces between Santa Fe and the other alliance members. 'There was an expectation that the budget cost would rise due to the change. But the alliance was by now robust enough to shoulder the problems of the participants and accepted that Santa Fe could be trusted to manage the new circumstances. Furthermore, the board was prepared to share the burden of extra costs if these became unavoidable, even though the drilling module was originally contracted under a fixed lump sum price.'

Santa Fe had anticipated a less co-operative response. 'Presenting a problem of this magnitude could traditionally have been met with contractual adversity followed by heavy client over-management,' Hinton points out. 'But on Andrew the change of plan was not analysed to death – we were trusted to provide a solution.'

The solution put forward by Santa Fe proposed that Far East Levingston Shipbuilding (FELS) in Singapore should be contracted to take over the design and construction subcontract. The new plan was underpinned by Santa Fe's long-term relationship with FELS and would follow an already proven route for design and construction of mobile drilling rigs. For Andrew, FELS would continue the compact modularised design and fabrication in Singapore under the supervision of Santa Fe, led by project manager Mike Kucharski, who later assumed the role of alliance manager for Santa Fe. All major equipment would be purchased through the drilling contractor's procurement subsidiary in Houston with support from the company's headquarters in Dallas. The Singapore site team included key members of Andrew's future drilling crew; a small Santa Fe team also operated within the main Andrew project team in London to address the interfaces with the integrated deck. Although the distant location of the module construction site gave rise to worries that the work would be carried out in relative isolation from the project, BP abided by its word not to institute man-for-man marking, relying on Santa Fe to run the job without a BP client representative in Singapore.

In the wake of the change a more pleasant surprise was in store for the alliance. After reviewing the task and change of scope in more detail, Santa Fe announced that it could deliver the Andrew drilling module not only on schedule, but for £350,000 less than originally budgeted. 'It was as though bad news was turned to good,' comments Hinton.

But the switch of subcontractors had delayed progress by several months, says Jerzak. 'The resulting schedule looked very tight. FELS began working on the design in July 1994 in readiness for fabrication to start early the next year, but construction was delayed until March while the design was taken to a more advanced level. This left only eight months to build and commission the module before it had to sail from Singapore.'

Soon after construction began FELS reconfirmed that it would meet the delivery

Drilling facilities loaded out in Singapore.

date. Fabrication of the module – the first North Sea fixed platform rig to be built by the Singapore yard – proceeded apace; by August 1995 the drilling facilities were ready for a month of operational trials by the Santa Fe drilling crew which would operate the rig onboard Andrew.

Once tested, the facilities were dismantled for transportation to Teesside, breaking the main modules down into subassemblies containing several minimodules to obtain structures of liftable weight for reassembly into the integrated deck. The move to Singapore had brought advantages in this respect; had fabrication been conducted in the USA under the original plan, the size of these structures would have been restricted by road transportation, causing full dismantling of the facilities into minimodules and a subsequently larger reassembly operation. Shipment by sea direct from FELS removed this constraint. Co-operation between Santa Fe, FELS and TJB developed a more efficient method for producing fewer, larger subassemblies, reducing the total number to six plus mast, with weights between 220t and 400t to make reassembly an easier operation.

Exchange of expertise among the alliance contractors also contributed to other improvements for the drilling facilities. Santa Fe advised TJB on tighter tolerances for fabricating the rig's skid beams to avoid difficulties sometimes encountered during offshore skidding, while during rig dismantling in Singapore, TJB requested all electrical cables be removed whole, rather than in sections to eliminate extensive

Subassemblies prepared for lifts into the integrated deck at Teesside.

Topsides
Drilling facilities

cable rejoining in Teesside. Santa Fe's site team also incorporated significant operational enhancements to a number of equipment items without asking for additional payment from the project. To assist in minimising offshore completion work, the 50m tall mast was redesigned to be lifted vertically as a single unit with all equipment installed, an action which enabled efficient temporary removal of the mast during the integrated deck's passage beneath the Transporter Bridge on the River Tees and its speedy reinstallation downriver at Hartlepool prior to the offshore tow. Structural analysis by Brown & Root also proved that internal bracing, included in the minimodule framing solely for sea transportation, could be removed onshore if additional minor external tie-downs were provided which did not need subsequent removal.

At the beginning of November the subassemblies were loaded onboard transportation vessel *Condock IV* in Singapore for the five-week voyage to Teesside via Suez. In mid-December, three weeks ahead of the scheduled delivery date, the drilling submodules were lifted into place atop Andrew's deck by the largest mobile crane in Britain, contracted for the purpose.

'The completion of the drilling module and the fit-for-purpose quality achieved within the time frame were remarkable achievements,' concludes Jerzak. 'A situation which could have had severe cost implications for the project had been converted into a major part of Andrew's success.'

Accommodation module

Andrew's 72-bed accommodation module was lifted into place on the integrated deck in mid-October 1995, six weeks ahead of schedule. Designed and fabricated by Emtunga of Sweden under an EPC contract, the module represented the first single-lift living quarters supplied by the company to the UK sector of the North Sea. Furthermore, the contract marked the first occasion BP and Emtunga had worked together, a co-operation which yielded significant advantages for the Andrew alliance.

Emtunga's entry into the UK offshore sector was preceded by a long track record in other offshore regions and in a variety of industries, during which time the company had developed a working culture closely suited to that sought by the Andrew project, as Emtunga alliance manager Sia Payani explains.

'Although Andrew was proposing a larger scale alliance, partnerships involving risk and reward concepts were not entirely new to us. At Emtunga we had developed an unusually close-knit relationship between management and workforce based on open communications – there have been no industrial disputes or strikes in our fifty-year history – and we also work with our key suppliers and subcontractors in an integrated team.

Accommodation module, arriving in Teesside onboard *Happy Buccaneer*, passing beneath the Transporter Bridge.

'When we tender for jobs all production departments take part, bidding on a risk and reward basis where they accept full responsibility for achieving cost and performance targets, and share collectively and individually for delivering under the cost target. Consequently our working pattern was already geared to match the behaviour and attitudes highlighted by Andrew's contractor selection process. This fact, plus our willingness to do something new and our competitive price, secured our place in the alliance team.'

Emtunga prepared a budget estimate for the accommodation module after joining the alliance in October 1993, to be delivered under a lump sum contract. As with other topsides lump sum contracts, those for living quarters also have a general reputation for running over budget, typically by 20% to 40%, largely due to late changes in workscope occurring during the fabrication stage.

To counteract this trend, the Andrew project team concentrated during preparation of the sanction estimate on identifying and deleting all unnecessary items with the potential to impact cost or schedule. The time available was also used to best advantage to exclude all contingencies normally added to the budget price as a precaution against anticipated changes in the living quarters caused by late requirements of the client or other topsides contractors. 'By co-operating across the interfaces that traditionally affect our workscope and ultimate costs, we attained a higher degree of confidence that the module design would not be changed later,' says Payani. By the time of sanction, the result of direct contact between the alliance members had enabled the cost of the accommodation module to be reduced by 10% to £5.6 million.

Emtunga developed a functional specification for the module, based upon the company's proven method of building submodules; these would be assembled to produce Andrew's four-storey living quarters. A system of lightweight partitions

Topsides
Accommodation module

– later adopted for other areas of the integrated deck – and extensive use of standard materials were central to the design. Innovation was also encouraged, with Emtunga successfully proposing that the substructure beneath the platform's aluminium helideck be constructed from the lightweight alloy, a change of course from BP's previous specifications.

Although the value of the accommodation module contract was the smallest of those in the alliance – reflected in Emtunga's opting for 1% of the gainshare – the company committed to Andrew's principles with enthusiasm. While the scope for achieving major cost reductions was more limited than on other contracts simply due to relative size, Emtunga continued to seek ways for extra savings in pursuit of best value for Andrew, even though its lump sum contract did not necessarily demand this.

Collaboration between the company and topsides designer Brown & Root brought several benefits. With an open flow of information between contractors, prices for materials to be used in the living quarters could be compared with those specified for other topsides applications. Although Brown & Root held responsibility for main procurement on the project, Emtunga's sources of materials provided cost advantages in some instances, typically saving up to 25%. Combining purchase orders to increase quantities also secured further reductions from suppliers.

'All support systems for the living quarters – for example electrical, communications, fire and gas, plus heating, ventilation and air conditioning (HVAC) – were provided from outside the module,' explains Brown & Root's Tony Ward, co-ordinating engineer for accommodation and drilling modules. 'To a large extent Emtunga had to rely on the work of others as the systems could not be fully tested until the module was installed and hooked up in the integrated deck. This created a very close working dependence and exchange of ideas between us.'

One key area of co-operation centred on safety. At the time of design, safety legislation in the UK was in transition from a regime of heavily prescriptive rules to a more modern approach based on a goal-setting philosophy, centred on an offshore safety case for all installations. For Andrew – the first manned fixed installation to pass through the complete cycle of design and operational safety cases – the cultural shift brought both challenges and opportunities.

The platform's temporary refuge (TR), a safe haven for control and decision making in the event of emergencies, is located within the deck structure directly below the accommodation unit. In addition to the central control room, one of the critical elements contained in the TR is the platform's HVAC system which must maintain a supply of breathable air to the TR should the outside environment be smoke filled. On Andrew this would be achieved by using the accommodation module as an air reservoir to provide a secondary supply of air to the TR and the mustered crew – an industry first. 'Predicting precise flow

Crane vessel Smit *Taklift IV* unloading (bottom left) and lifting accommodation module into the integrated deck, six weeks ahead of schedule.

characteristics during recirculation of air between TR and accommodation was a significant engineering challenge,' says Ward, 'one which can not be fully validated until tested on the full scale. There was the risk that changes might be necessary to the module at a late stage. In the event, the design work and trials we carried out with Emtunga kept us on the right track and major modifications were avoided.'

A mock-up of one of Andrew's cabins was fabricated at Emtunga's Vara works to investigate air flow characteristics; optimisation of the module's fire and smoke detection and firewater sprinkler systems came in for close scrutiny. Under the UK's outgoing safety legislation, prescriptive safety rules had dictated that firewater sprinklers were required throughout accommodation units. With traditional practice open to challenge, the case was made by Brown & Root that universal sprinklers were unnecessary on the grounds that an array of other fire detection and protection measures were included in the module, and that sprinklers improved safety only in certain areas, for example in the galley and laundry.

'First reactions were understandably sceptical in some quarters, as on the surface it appeared Andrew's cost cutting motives were threatening to jeopardise safety,' emphasises lead architectural engineer Rob Skivington, who along with Tony Ward initiated the proposal under Andrew's Opportunities for Improvement scheme. 'But by practical demonstration supported by rigorous quantitative risk analysis, the project proved that rapid detection and evacuation from cabins was more effective in enhancing personal safety than

Topsides
Accommodation module

waiting for sprinklers to come into action, a case accepted by the regulatory authority.' As a secondary benefit, the reduced number of strategically distributed sprinklers brought savings of almost £100,000 to the project.

'By co-operating across the interfaces that traditionally affect our work and costs, we attained a higher degree of confidence that the module design would not be changed later'

Sia Payani
Alliance project manager Emtunga

Fabrication of the module was carried out by Emtunga in two locations, beginning in August 1994 at the company's Vara facility where the smaller submodules were manufactured on a high-efficiency computerised production line employing less than twenty fabricators. Once completed the sections were transported to Emtunga's Gothenburg yard where they were assembled to produce the finished accommodation module, measuring 27m by 10.5m and 15m high, and weighing 520t including aluminium helideck.

'Andrew's policy of trusting the alliance contractors to apply self-inspection and quality management were ideal for Emtunga,' says BRO John Jerzak. 'The company's small established teams were experienced in taking responsibility and working without client supervision. Where before BP might have had a dozen full-time site representatives to follow the work in Sweden, for the accommodation module no client team was involved. Product quality remained high, costs were kept within budget, and schedule was never a problem.'

Indeed timing of the module's delivery became a major contribution to the overall success of the integrated deck. As the project's plan to maximise onshore completion began to advance, the need was identified for the accommodation module to be installed ahead of its scheduled December 1995 date in order to ease congestion of activities in Teesside and permit the full commissioning of all utility systems. Consequently, in June of that year the project requested delivery one month early. 'With only six months remaining to delivery such a move would have been certain to result in claims for extra costs on conventional projects,' Jerzak comments.

Instead, as a clear demonstration of its commitment to the alliance and Andrew's success, Emtunga agreed it could not only accelerate the programme, it would do so for no extra cost and would even beat the new deadline. In mid-October, six weeks ahead of the original plan, the accommodation module was lifted into place in the integrated deck. When asked how Emtunga responded to the alliance's seemingly tall order, Payani simply replies: 'We just said yes.' Setting and surpassing stretched targets had become a habit on Andrew.

Onshore completion – 110%

Within Andrew's catalogue of hard earned successes, the completion of the integrated deck onshore at Teesside is seen by the project as one of its greatest accomplishments, indeed perhaps at the apex of tangible triumphs for behavioural change and teamworking. For not only did the completion strategy lead directly to the largest single saving for the alliance – reducing offshore hookup costs by £20 million and cutting over six months out of the time to first oil – the onshore achievement reversed the industry's common experience of project cost escalation in the offshore phase.

Included in Andrew's sanctioned target cost was a sum of £24 million earmarked for offshore hookup and commissioning of the platform – by the time the platform was to be installed in 1996, that figure would have escalated to £27 million measured as money of the day. Following normal offshore working methods it looked likely that a flotel supporting a workforce numbering several hundreds would conduct the operation over a six month period to the then first oil target date of January 1997.

'The offshore phase presented a serious risk for anticipated costs to rise on Andrew, just as they have done on almost all other platform projects,' states BP's Roy Timms, responsible as completions manager for co-ordinating onshore and offshore completions programmes. 'Precisely defining the scope of work which will be carried out offshore has always been difficult, primarily because the targets for onshore commissioning are rarely met, generating an unpredictable quantity of carry-over work. Unfinished tasks have tended to mount up, causing offshore manhours to grow almost out of control. When you consider that offshore work

'The offshore phase presented a serious risk for anticipated costs to escalate on Andrew, just as they have done on almost all other platform projects'

Roy Timms
Completions manager BP

Platform control room in operation at Teesside.

Topsides
Onshore completion – 110%

is around ten times more costly, you can see why the large contingency sums allocated to projects are normally eaten away.'

For a topsides of Andrew's size, history would forecast that the £27 million offshore budget would rise to well over £50 million, consuming a large portion of the project's £39 million unallocated provision. Although the project had started out with the intention of minimising offshore work and achieving one hundred percent onshore completion, it was recognised that all projects in the recent past had embraced the same worthy aims, only to witness the topsides depart from the construction site in a state of completion well below that expected. Something very different was required if Andrew was to avoid falling into the same trap.

From the early days of the project, the alliance had accepted that rather than adhere to convention and bring onboard a specialist hookup contractor, the companies in the alliance would find a way to combine their skills to undertake the offshore work. In doing so, the detailed familiarity built up within the team would be exploited to best advantage in a natural continuation, and would also eliminate the introduction of another interface, one which would not necessarily be aligned to Andrew's goals thereby exposing the alliance to uncontrolled costs. The entire operations team which would eventually run the platform during production would also be fully involved throughout commissioning to create ownership of the topsides and reduce the learning curve offshore. And the commissioning programme, normally confined to a few months at the end of construction, would be pulled forward to begin much earlier, overlapping ongoing fabrication activities.

'Originally the plan for Andrew's commissioning did not seem too radically different from other projects,' comments Steve Selby, topsides commissioning manager for TJB. 'With so much happening at the start of a development, commissioning tends to be viewed as a separate activity a long way off. In TJB's initial manhours, some four months commissioning had been allowed, where we would act effectively as assistants to the client's operating team in the traditional way – we knew this was too short and would lead to the usual problems. But by virtue of our early involvement in the alliance team, we were able to influence Andrew's plan, doubling the length of time for commissioning activities at site.'

'By virtue of our early involvement we were able to influence Andrew's plan, doubling the length of time for commissioning activities at site'

Steve Selby
Commissioning manager TJB

September 1995 was set as the start date for commissioning, eight months before topsides sailaway. But more crucially, it was agreed at the time of sanction that design and fabrication programmes would be led from the outset by the commissioning schedule. By developing a detailed plan for commissioning, realistic need dates for design deliverables and equipment packages were determined, the latter dovetailing with Andrew's innovative drive to interact in a mature and openly more trusting way with the project's multitude of equipment and materials suppliers.

But according to BP completions engineer Brian Gebruers, the shift of emphasis to onshore commissioning was something of an uphill struggle at first. 'The goal behind the initiative was to minimise offshore work by designing it out of the project from the beginning. This entailed challenging many common practices which assumed certain tasks would be performed offshore, and that the definition of those tasks could be left until later. It appeared to designers they were being criticised for leaving offshore work in the design, and this naturally met with some resistance. The key was getting the message across that offshore minimisation *was* part of the design function on Andrew. Once the benefits started to show, the challenges became easier and the offshore manhours began to fall.'

Step by step the minimisation effort gathered momentum, at first involving designers and fabricators, followed by input from installation contractor Saipem. The word completion was deliberately used to give access to all phases of the project, rather than confine attention to traditional commissioning activities alone. The alliance was steadily aligning itself, moving from the concept of simply maximising onshore commissioning to the firm belief that Andrew could achieve an extraordinary offshore result.

One yardstick for measuring progress towards that achievement is by considering the ratio of manhours of offshore work required to complete each tonne of installed topsides. In the early 1980s in the North Sea, the topsides of oil production platforms – then most frequently of modularised design – commonly required over 100 manhours per tonne to complete. A case in point is BP's Magnus platform, taking 150 manhours per tonne, translating to over 4.5 million manhours in total. By the 1990s offshore manhours had roughly halved, but even with the advent of large integrated decks, notable exceptions still occurred, highlighting the threat which offshore work poses to project budgets.

In 1994, Total's Dunbar platform pushed the ratio to a new lower limit, notching up an outstanding 20 manhours per tonne for its 9100t integrated deck. Though a significant achievement in its own right, the Dunbar performance was to serve only as a challenge to Andrew in its quest to become the most successful project in the North Sea, leading the alliance to set a still more difficult target, says Timms.

'At sanction we gave ourselves the task of beating the best in class by reducing offshore work to only 10 manhours per tonne. At that point in time we had no known mechanism for getting to such a level, but as we learned the knack of homing in on stretched targets one pace at a time, the possibility of meeting – and more surprisingly, even beating this goal – drew within our reach.'

Designing out offshore work
Key actions

All caissons fixed in the jacket and structural connections to integrated deck minimised

Firewater pumps installed in caissons

70% reduction in original underdeck riser tie-in work

Deck deflection analysis confirmed major equipment pipework disconnection to be unnecessary for deck lift

Majority of platform liquid storage tanks filled prior to transportation

Elevation of lift spreader bars raised to permit onshore installation of major equipment

Flare tower interface raised to allow onshore installation of compressor exhausts

Drilling mast installed onshore

Equipment cabinet tie-downs designed for both transportation and operation

Seafastenings designed to minimise offshore hot work

Topsides
Onshore completion – 110%

So successful was the stepwise strategy in eroding offshore work that by November 1994, a little over a year since the project had put forward its target cost, estimated offshore manhours had been slashed to around 10,000 in total, an order of magnitude better than even the stretched target. Now armed with an unprecedented detailed knowledge of the offshore workscope eighteen months before sailaway, the completions team had the confidence to take the strategy one major step further with the proposal that no flotel would be required to support the offshore operation.

An idea which at first appeared to be pushing the concept of stretched targets beyond all reasonable limits was in fact founded on sound reasoning. With offshore work now severely diminished, the need for a large workforce had also disappeared, and rather than facing six months offshore, first oil seemed attainable in a quarter of that time. If Andrew's deck could be completed to an exceptionally advanced state onshore, then within a relatively short time after installation it should be able to support its own platform workforce for the run to first oil, dispensing with a costly flotel.

Once committed to the 'no-flotel' strategy the alliance set about evaluating the logistics to achieve its revolutionary approach to bringing onstream a lift-installed North Sea platform. The key to the solution lay in Saipem's heavy lift vessel *S7000* which after installing the platform would remain on station for a limited time as the offshore construction and completion support base. With capacity to accommodate up to 800 people, the vessel would enable an alliance workforce to complete essential hookup tasks and render Andrew certifiably fit for habitation and drilling. Although *S7000* presented a more expensive alternative to a flotel on a daily basis, if the support period could be of sufficiently short duration the economics of the plan would be favourable. That plan called for Andrew to be certified for habitation within two days of installation to permit the operations crew and workforce to take up residence on the platform. With *S7000* alongside, the remainder of the hookup work would be completed within a week, allowing the vessel then to leave the field and the standalone platform, accommodating up to 72 people, to continue to prepare for production.

Now, with what was undoubtedly a bold offshore strategy in place – to outside observers it may have appeared to be something of an untried gamble – the alliance realised it had again created an opportunity to stretch its overall targets still further. In early 1995, with concerted attention to offshore completion plans continuing to drive hookup manhours down below the already record-setting level of one manhour per tonne, the alliance reviewed and retargeted its goals for Andrew.

'Since soon after sanction we had been working to a target of first oil in September 1996 and an outturn cost of £320 million,' states project manager John Martin. 'Bringing production forward by four months and cost down by over £50 million had seemed almost unreachable at the time, but now not only could we see our way to achieving this, the vision had opened up for surpassing it. It would have been easy to leave things as they were and coast home with a good measure of success. But we had declared that we would be the most successful oilfield investment in the UK to date and wanted to reinforce this by pushing ourselves even further. We had given ourselves licence to generate our own tensions; this was our choice, no-one levered it onto us.'

In consequence, the Andrew challenge was reaffirmed. First oil date was pulled forward to mid-July 1996 accompanied by a new target cost of £290 million, potentially cutting oil delivery time by six months and sanctioned development cost by over 20%. To the alliance partners, likely rewards stemming from the gainshare agreement had grown beyond all expectations.

While economic advantages were clearly apparent, the strategy was double-edged in that it shifted an array of difficult offshore tasks to a far safer onshore location. Offshore working is inherently hazardous, particularly during the complex construction activities of prolonged hookup programmes with underdeck operations above sea level. Consequently a plan which minimised offshore hookup and commissioning with associated reduced exposure to risk, would find ready support from the regulatory body – the Health & Safety Executive (HSE) – plus the certifying authority for the project, Lloyd's Register.

'This was a big prize we were chasing,' Timms reflects. 'The economic savings were attractive but equally important was the step change this would make to safety. But it had not been done before and required the total co-operation of all parties in the preparation and execution of a very detailed plan. We had to bring together all of the interests from design to operations, plus the certifying

Onshore completion transfered an array of difficult offshore tasks to the safer onshore location.

Topsides
Onshore completion – 110%

'This was a big prize we were chasing. The economic advantages of onshore completion were attractive but equally important was the step change this would make to safety'

Roy Timms
Completions manager BP

Topsides
Onshore completion – 110%

authority and the safety regulator. Maintaining a sharp focus on the goal of maximising onshore work was a vital ingredient – to promote this we invented the ideal of 110% completion.'

Challenging minds to grapple with a notional concept – 'how can you have more than 100% complete?' – achieved its exact purpose in raising and sustaining the profile of Andrew's commitment of reaching a state of completion onshore that had never before been realised by any North Sea project. The idea permeated the entire project at all locations and became a watchword for Andrew's drive towards unparalleled success – the old phrase of 100% commissioning was no longer sufficient. The 110% concept encompassed total mechanical completion of the integrated deck but drove beyond this to include all systems being fully commissioned and working, and handed over to the operations team onshore – such acceptance would normally come only after offshore hookup. Furthermore the asset operations team would demonstrate to HSE all operational and safety systems onshore and their interface with Andrew's operational safety case. And as a culmination of the achievement, the project would seek to obtain a 'draft Certificate of Fitness' from Lloyd's Register with only specific minimum limitations remaining to be addressed offshore, at which time the installation could be granted its full certificate.

Although the completion plan was centred on bringing offshore work to the onshore location, by no means did this imply that extensive offshore manhours would also be transferred. The effort injected into designing out offshore work paid off, greatly reducing the overall labour content of delivering a completed integrated deck. Comparisons of the onshore and offshore approaches in terms of manhours saved is not directly possible as the tasks involved became substantially different due to the integrated nature of the onshore work. However, as a guide, one estimate suggests that the added onshore impact amounted to no more than 10,000 manhours at Port Clarence, a relatively small amount compared to the project's £3.5 million onshore commissioning budget, and a marked decrease in the originally expected offshore workload of over 100,000 manhours.

The fundamental method for controlling the completions work divided the integrated deck into five areas, identified as utilities, accommodation, drilling, wellbay and process. Activities in these areas were phased by systems and subsystems – over 230 in all – to structure the handover from construction to commissioning teams. Priorities were also attached to the areas, with utilities heading the list and followed by process, to enable full commissioning in one completion area while fabrication and fit-out work continued in others.

To ensure systems and subsystems were comprehensive and accurate in their contents, a new method was developed for allocating tagged items – such as

pumps, instruments and cables – to the appropriate completions system. Until now this activity had been primarily a manual effort on the part of commissioning engineers, one which required extensive updating, often allowing inaccuracies to creep in.

'For Andrew the process and instrument drawings were produced using an intelligent computer aided design system which linked the drawings to engineering databases,' says BP completions engineer Yaniv Melitz. 'By extending the function of this system we were able to meet completion requirements far more effectively. Boundaries could be added to the drawings which automatically allocated all enclosed tagged items and associated equipment into the completion subsystem, a procedure which could be readily repeated if drawings changed. This greatly reduced manhours expended and improved accuracy compared with the conventional method.'

Tied in closely to the programme was the timed arrival of equipment packages. 'The performance of suppliers to Andrew was exceptional,' observes commissioning manager Steve Selby. 'On other projects the normal routine involves a package arriving at site with a box of bits that the commissioning team has to install before the equipment will work. The project's supplier initiative pushed hard to change this so that packages were truly finished at the manufacturer's works. We tried for perfection and of course a few fell short of the mark, but of the 130 major packages over 90% were better than we'd ever seen before.'

The completions team was also structured differently from conventional commissioning groups, including two particularly notable departures from standard practice. Total team size numbered only around fifty without the 'business as usual' duplication of a large client supervision team and 'endless men being thrown at the job', many of whom would concentrate on producing punch lists of carry-over work for offshore hookup. The other key difference was that BP's operations crew, responsible for running Andrew as a producing asset, were included as members of the completions team, accounting for over half its strength and reporting to TJB's commissioning manager rather than acting as a separate force.

'Normal procedure during commissioning is for the operations group to witness the commissioning of plant and equipment, with formal handover not taking place until everything has been hooked up, tested and proven offshore,' says BP offshore installation manager Vince Rendall. 'It's not the most efficient interface and is often contentious. We tackled the problem on Andrew by setting up area ownership teams, allocating to operations supervisors and technicians areas of responsibility on the platform for which they were fully involved in the commissioning procedure, working within the operations team as well as with

Key onshore completion activities

Flow testing and proving of all utility and process systems, including running main power generators and operating gas compressors on nitrogen/helium mixture

Total system nitrogen leak testing without further offshore trials

Drilling facilities re-established and part certified for use

Occupation of the fully operational and functioning accommodation unit

All fabrication activities (structural, architectural, thermal insulation, fire proofing, protective coatings) certified complete

Safety equipment and systems demonstrated and certified ready for use

Emergency shutdown system function tested

Achievement of 'draft Certificate of Fitness' from certifying authority

Topsides
Onshore completion – 110%

additional TJB technician and vendor support as required. Ownership of the topsides by the operations crew grew from this – it was in the interest of all individuals to ensure their areas were fully functioning onshore.'

His views are echoed by operations supervisor Tommy Thornton. 'Traditionally we were perceived around the site as 'orange coats', hanging about, changing small items to justify our existence – so there was a deal of resistance to overcome at first. This way is far better – we gain more hands-on experience of the kit than just by writing documents, then feed that practical knowledge back into fit-for-purpose procedures. As we have helped commission the plant we already know that it works; the handover to operations no longer involves volumes of paperwork and punch lists, it's a simple acceptance.'

Similar teams made up of contractors and operators were assigned to complete the drilling facilities, with Santa Fe's core offshore drilling team leading the onshore activities, while for the accommodation module, hotel contractor Aramark continued the commissioning work it had begun in Sweden. In all instances the drive was to build knowledge and ownership during the onshore completion of the integrated deck which would smooth the transition to early oil production. As a major contribution to the process of 110% completion, Lloyd's Register agreed to bring forward the mobilisation of its offshore surveyors into the completions phase to verify and witness all onshore completions activities.

'We supplied three surveyors to site to witness the onshore testing,' states LR's project manager David Cummergen. 'The main objective was to minimise the degree of retesting of systems normally called for offshore. By being fully conversant with the plant and systems we were also in a position to list the remaining offshore work as limitations to the Certificate of Fitness – this was an entirely new approach on Andrew and was designed to make offshore completion more efficient. The offshore team knew precisely what was expected of them to lift the final limitations to achieve certificates for habitation, drilling and production.'

'The offshore team knew precisely what was expected of them to lift the final limitations to achieve certificates for habitation, drilling and production'

David Cummergen
Lloyd's Register

By the end of 1995, three months into commissioning, the utilities area was nearing completion. As planned, the operations crew took up residence in the fully functioning accommodation module in January 1996, working seven-day shifts as though offshore, including 24-hour manning of the central control room. The move provided a clear signal to the project that the completions strategy was functioning extremely effectively. 'Hot and cold in every room five months before sailaway. Remarkable,' quips Selby.

With confidence in the ascendant, the team looked again at the project schedule. The progress of tie-back and other drilling equipment trials at Teesside had revealed opportunities to shorten the offshore work programme yet again. Three more weeks were cut out of the plan, accelerating production of first oil from the field to 21 June that year.

The concept of 110% completion was not restricted to the full working of plant and systems. Equally important was the demonstration of the asset operations team's competence, achieved by replicating as closely as possible the activities and demands of an operational platform to the satisfaction of the alliance and industry authorities.

As other systems and areas of the integrated deck followed utilities to completion, the operations crew prepared for its one-week onshore demonstration to Lloyd's Register and the Health and Safety Executive in April 1996. After proving the full operation of the platform's systems, particular attention was paid to emergency response scenarios. Based upon the severest incidents identified by quantitative risk analysis for Andrew's safety case, the team conducted a series of realistic exercises – including activation of fire and deluge systems, emergency control room operation and firefighting – under assessment by the independent Offshore Petroleum Industry Training Board. The demonstrations were both thorough and realistic, extending to the arrival of a helicopter from RAF Kinloss to establish radio communications with the platform and complete the emergency evacuation exercise by winching a man from the helideck.

On 10 April, after successfully demonstrating both the safe operation of all systems and competence of the asset operations team the Andrew alliance received its 'draft Certificate of Fitness' from Lloyd's Register, the first of its kind achieved in the industry. Eleven days later, in a three-hour loadout operation, the 9620t integrated deck was transferred by sixteen groups of trailers from the Port Clarence quayside to the *Giant 4* transportation barge, ready for the first short leg of its journey to the Andrew field.

Travelling only a few miles downriver, the deck was berthed at Hartlepool where the drilling mast and top section of the platform's crane – removed for passage under the historic Transporter Bridge at Port Clarence – were re-installed as planned. In addition to the lifting operations, the one-week stay at the quayside was used to good effect by the TJB team to complete late-occurring modification work to seafastenings and HVAC systems in the drilling facilities. When the integrated deck sailed from Hartlepool toward the Moray Firth on 8 May, the deck was essentially complete.

'The sailaway date had remained unaltered throughout the entire project from 1993,' observes topsides BRO Mike Brown. 'To meet that date together with the extreme challenge of 110% onshore completion, is a singular achievement in the industry for which the entire project, and particularly TJB, can be justifiably proud.'

Meeting the schedule and building a fully-functioning topsides onshore were married to another formidable accomplishment; the cost for fabricating and commissioning the integrated deck onshore had come in £1 million under budget.

The operations crew took up residence in the fully functioning accommodation module three months before topsides sailaway.

Onshore demonstrations

Plant start-up, running and function testing of all shutdown levels

Emergency response

Safety systems operation

Operation of permit to work system

Maintenance activities

Use of asset information and support systems, plus full communications with BP operations base in Aberdeen

Topsides
Onshore completion – 110%

'The traditional threat of fabrication growth had been identified as our primary enemy from the outset – remember that the planned direct 1.4 million manhours would very likely have increased to around 2 million on a similar sized deck in the past,' reminds TJB alliance manager Brian Colpitts.

'For Andrew we were successful in holding to our estimates for the base scope of work, coming in at 1.43 million direct manhours. This must also be viewed in the context of including full commissioning of the topsides to a degree never before achieved.'

Compared with similar topsides built in Teesside over the previous five years, over 30% had been sliced from manhour levels, and this for a deck which in the process had also surpassed all normal measures of onshore commissioning. Although some disciplines had overrun the very tight manhour budgets set for Andrew – piping, electrical and fireproofing among them – the growth had been drastically reduced in relation to preceding projects. Other disciplines had

'For Andrew we were successful in holding to our estimates for the base scope of work, including full commissioning of the topsides to a degree never before achieved'

Brian Colpitts
Alliance manager TJB

achieved reductions, the overall effect being one of marked progress away from 'business as usual'.

By holding manhours growth down and minimising costs across the range of other reimbursable items also covered by its contract, TJB secured an overall reduction in cost compared with the sanctioned estimate of £53.8 million. 'Under a conventional contract it's unlikely a fabricator would have had the incentive to pursue these possibilities,' notes BP project co-ordinator Paul Bibby. 'The spirit of the alliance and the potential gainshare made the difference to obtaining best value for Andrew.'

Construction manhours savings (%)
Compared with recently constructed similar decks

Electrical & instrumentation	7%	Structural drawings	38%
Pipe fabrication	15%	Structural erection	45%
Heating, ventilation and air conditioning	21%	Pipe erection	46%
Passive fire protection	22%	Painting	48%
Structural fabrication	31%	**Overall project saving**	**31%**

During the course of fabrication, TJB also undertook additional work above the base scope. Valued at some £3.6 million and transferred from other budgets within the alliance, the company's increased scope included onshore hookup of drilling submodules, minor modifications to living quarters and vendor packages, and the reworking of piping and cable systems caused by defective materials. Although the increased scope could have jeopardised the fabrication schedule, the company incorporated the unplanned load into its programme, completed the work and met the original sailaway date.

But contractual performance alone does not tell the whole story, adds Bibby. 'There is no doubt that dispatching a completed deck to the field directly enabled us to avoid expending £20 million during offshore hookup,' he notes. 'But to arrive at that achievement required the whole alliance to plan and perform together – throughout design, procurement, fabrication, commissioning, installation and hookup – without spending additional money. It is an outstanding result which could only arise from a true alignment of interests and commitment of the entire team.'

As Andrew's integrated deck headed for the open sea, the alliance faced the final set of tests in its self-belief. The offshore completion strategy, upon which the ultimate achievements for Andrew now rested, had been progressed to an unprecedented level, targeting hookup and completion in only 7000 manhours. Rather than measure offshore hookup in tens of manhours per tonne as dictated thus far by even the best in North Sea history, Andrew's plan was measured in minutes.

'To dispatch a completed deck to the field is an outstanding result which could only arise from a true alignment of interests and commitment of the entire team'

Paul Bibby
Project co-ordinator BP

Beneath the waves

'Accepting responsibility for your own decisions suited our team, although we had to adjust to the 'no client' situation'

Eric Van Baars
Alliance manager Allseas

Hidden from view beneath the North Sea, Andrew's array of subsea structures, equipment and pipelines extends over 60km to link with the main export routes for transporting the field's oil and gas production. While the platform's topsides and jacket had been growing onshore, work had been ongoing offshore to complete the underwater facilities in readiness for the platform's arrival. Though out of sight on the seabed, the contribution from pipelines and subsea engineering to the project's success is far from hidden, with some £10 million in savings arising from innovation, challenges to accepted practice, and co-operation within the alliance.

Oil is exported from the Andrew platform through a 16km long 10-inch diameter pipeline, teeing into the existing Brae pipeline for transportation through the Forties system to Cruden Bay in Scotland. Gas flows in the opposite direction via a 44km long 8-inch line to join the CATS (Central Area Transmission System) pipeline, terminating in Teesside. Closely linked to Andrew's subsea facilities are those for the nearby Cyrus oilfield, developed in parallel with Andrew under a separate alliance between BP and main contractor Rockwater.

Within the Andrew alliance, Brown & Root held responsibility for design of the pipelines and subsea facilities, while Allseas – joining as final alliance member to complete the group's capabilities – would procure and install the two export pipelines. During the course of the project, a diving alliance would be formed for which Rockwater would execute all diving work and commissioning for both Andrew and Cyrus developments.

'We were hooked on Andrew's way of working from the start,' says Allseas alliance manager, Eric Van Baars. 'Accepting responsibility for your own decisions suited our team, although we had to adjust to the 'no client' situation. For example, similar to those of other contractors, Allseas management systems had evolved on the basis of client approval – these had to be reinvented for Andrew.'

Within the project's target cost approved at sanction, pipelines accounted for £39.6 million. Within this, Allseas' contract was split between a lump sum for procuring and laying the lines, and a schedule of rates covering trenching, diving work, subsea structures and other materials. The company opted for a 4% stake in the gainshare.

Savings on pipeline and subsea costs had begun during the presanction phase, with Brown & Root's designers responding to their newfound freedom to question existing engineering solutions.

'Subsea equipment came in for early scrutiny,' states Mike McSherry, Brown & Root's pipelines and subsea manager for the project. 'The two main subsea structures protecting the Brae and CATS pipeline tie-ins were reanalysed to determine potential loads which could arise if snagged by fishing nets. The design was rationalised to produce a snag-free profile which together with further soils evaluation led to the elimination of conventional foundation piles. The new designs, incorporating skirt plates and mudmats, reduced structural steel by half to a total of 140t and brought savings of £500,000.'

Another 60t structure, planned to house the subsea isolation valves (SSIVs) required in the export pipelines, was also critically reviewed. Instead, by incorporating the valves into the towhead structure for the Cyrus bundle, a separate SSIV structure became unnecessary, yielding £800,000 savings, in this case shared equally by the two projects.

'We identified opportunities to make improvements in response to the open invitation to enhance Andrew's design and the project's economics,' recounts Brown & Root lead subsea engineer Christine Benfield. 'There was no automatic acceptance that the best solutions had already been determined during the conceptual stage and we were encouraged to review all elements of the work critically; the Opportunities for Improvement scheme added incentive to this and promoted a degree of healthy internal competition. A key factor was that for once we had sufficient time in the design stage to apply our knowledge more fully – the benefits for Andrew soon followed.'

Subsea pipeline protection structure being lowered to the seabed.

Beneath the waves

Subsea protection structure.

'Even a distant remark could flow into the Andrew organisation and work its way up to a decision'

Peter Olden
Project engineer Allseas

At the time of sanction the project had kept open its options on the choice of route for the gas export line. A flexible approach to negotiations on gas sales and transportation led to an agreement for use of the Amoco-operated CATS pipeline, bringing to Andrew the twin benefits of a shorter gas export route compared with the main alternative, plus more favourable seabed conditions which looked likely to assist trenching operations during installation. Savings of the order of £2 million resulted. Additional reductions ensued as the team secured the shortest practical route through adjacent licence blocks by negotiation with other operators.

Permitting design engineers to be involved in third party discussions developed an awareness of factors outside the project which had direct bearing on Andrew's facilities. Interaction with Amoco concerning pipeline entry specifications gave rise to a challenge from Brown & Root's process engineers on the diameter of Andrew's gas line, demonstrating that this could be operated at the higher pressure of 210 bar and still fall within the design criteria of CATS. The approach – which also entailed the successful enrolment of the Health & Safety Executive – enabled the gas export line to be reduced from 10in to 8in diameter, cutting a further £1 million from Andrew's proposed expenditure.

Peter Olden, then project engineer and later alliance manager for Allseas, points to instances where cross-party co-operation helped identify other cost-reducing measures. 'Although the tie-in spool and valve assembly required by Amoco was 30in diameter, the actual bore of the valve was only 24in, hence we proposed that the entire assembly could be based on the smaller size. This was accepted and netted £350,000 savings for the project. All of this stemmed from an observation made by the subcontractor engaged to dry the gas pipeline, showing that on Andrew even a 'distant remark' could flow into the organisation and work its way up to a decision. Traditionally, contractors would not have bothered to pursue such changes.'

Allseas had already demonstrated its commitment to the alliance by offering to lay the pipelines in 1995 – originally planned for 1996 – while deferring payment according to the later schedule. The availability of an earlier operational window to carry out the work reduced the risk of subsequent project delays. Other co-operative actions were to follow. While surveying the pipeline route in 1994, the company also deployed its vessel to survey the predrilling template site on behalf of Saipem, and thereafter for Rockwater along the Cyrus bundle route, thereby engaging one vessel instead of three. Workscope exchange also featured: although purchase of subsea ball and check valves was covered in Allseas' scope of work, the task was handed over to Brown & Root's procurement department which through fit-for-purpose specifications and reduced documentation and inspection requirements delivered the valves for £550,000 less.

Collaboration between Allseas, Brown & Root and British Steel paved the way for the application of innovative technology, notching up the first use of high frequency induction (HFI) welded pipe for hydrocarbon production service in the

North Sea. The project's lead pipeline engineer, Nasser Bordbar of Brown & Root, describes the background. 'Conventional seamless pipe, sourced from overseas, was to be used to fabricate Andrew's export lines. However, at relatively small diameters this can exhibit variations in wall thickness and other characteristics, sometimes sufficient to slow down pipelaying productivity, hence an alternative solution was presented. From its new facility in Hartlepool, British Steel was able to manufacture pipe to much tighter tolerances by seam-welding steel strip using HFI technology. The process provided very close control over wall thicknesses such that we were able to specify a thinner walled pipe, which over a distance of 60km of pipelines amounted to savings around £500,000.'

Pipe quality played an important part in maintaining high productivity during offshore installation, an operation which again saw Andrew move away from industry traditions.

Pipelaying by Allseas' vessel *Lorelay* began in April 1995. The alliance's policy of minimising client intervention and duplication of effort obviated the need for the usual client compliance team onboard to 'look over the shoulder of the installation contractor throughout every shift' as a check on welding procedures and quality. Allseas was entrusted to perform to an equally high standard without client intervention, carrying out inspection and quality assurance as a matter of self-regulation.

'Normally there's a debate offshore between client and contractor over every pipe joint – any 'grey' areas are subject to welding repair,' says Allseas' Olden. 'We felt confident that our own inspection procedures plus the higher quality of steel pipe we were using would cut down on this. The Health & Safety Executive was concerned at first with BP's hands-off approach but the alliance stuck to its case. With two Allseas radiographers present, plus periodic offshore audits by BP and HSE, the regulator was satisfied that high quality would be maintained. In the event we received top marks from the regulator and in addition pipelaying efficiency went up.'

Over a thirty day period, Andrew's two export pipelines were successfully fabricated and installed on the seabed in a high-productivity operation, reaching maximum daily pipelay rates of over 6km for the gas line and almost 4km for the larger oil line.

Once laid, the lines were trenched and in the case of the oil line, backfilled. The initial plan for the oil line called for the conventional practice of laying the pipe on the seabed, followed by trenching and backfilling to provide both thermal insulation and stability against the phenomenon of upheaval buckling caused by expansion as hot oil flows through the line. While the project was considering the option of coating the pipeline to provide insulation, it was also recognised that if a minimum depth of backfill cover of 0.6m above the pipe could be guaranteed at all

Onboard pipelay vessel *Lorelay*.

Beneath the waves

Pipelines and subsea
Key savings for
Andrew and Cyrus

Optimised tie-in location
and route to gas export line

Gas pipeline diameter reduced

Subsea structures rationalised

Smaller tie-in equipment

Fit-for-purpose subsea valves

High frequency induction
welded pipe

Andrew SSIVs installed in
Cyrus towhead

Trenching and backfill
efficiencies improved

Engineering innovation
enhanced bundle fabrication

Diving alliance formed to
optimise work across the projects

points along its length, additional insulation coating would be unnecessary.

'The key issue was to achieve a very smooth profile in the trench at sufficient depth to provide the backfill cover,' explains Olden. 'But control of seabed trenching operations can be difficult. Imperfections in the trench often lead to free spans occurring below the pipeline, which if left unfilled can overstress the line and therefore need correction. Or the trench may be too shallow in some places which requires additional rockdumping on the line to attain the stability. On top of this there was the uncertainty of soft clays along the route which could have caused problems for the trenching equipment.'

To determine the true nature of the task and prove that sufficient backfill could be achieved to avoid pipe insulation coating, Allseas initiated early trenching and backfilling trials in the Andrew field in May 1994 – at no added cost to the alliance. The company's *Trenchsetter* vessel successfully demonstrated that by carefully controlling the rate of trenching, a uniform trench over two metres deep could be attained, proving that the specified backfilling could be accomplished throughout to dispense with pipeline insulation coating.

When the actual operation followed a year later, designer and installer worked together offshore to maximise the benefits of the approach. 'As the pipelines were trenched, Allseas carried out a subsea survey every three kilometres and fed the results directly to the design team,' recounts Bordbar, who was onboard *Trenchsetter* for the operation. 'We then assessed on the spot whether any span corrections or rock dumping were necessary. But the trenching control had provided the smooth profile; no second pass was needed to correct spans and no rock dumping was required to supplement backfilling.'

The improved trenching technique proved its worth over the six-week operation. Although the trenching rate itself was slower, the elimination of rework

Improved pipeline trenching
techniques achieved by *Trenchsetter*
helped to eliminate oil pipeline
insulation coating.

resulted in a faster job overall. This, together with pipe coating savings, presented the alliance with a healthy £1.8 million reduction.

'Working in the Andrew alliance was a pleasure,' remarks Olden. 'There was no need for the usual games between client and contractors. We could free our minds of commercial conflicts and concentrate instead on making major decisions together for the project's benefit.'

'We could free our minds of commercial conflicts and concentrate instead on making major decisions together for the project's benefit'

Peter Olden
Project engineer Allseas

Cyrus satellite

Lying between seven and ten kilometres north of Andrew in Block 16/28, the small Cyrus field was also under development in parallel with the main field. Cyrus had already been in production for a two-year period until March 1992, with two wells producing oil through BP's oil production vessel *Seillean*. But with an upgrade in reserves to some 25 million barrels, the field came in line for redevelopment, requiring two new horizontal wells to be drilled in the southwest of the field, completed subsea and tied back to the production facilities on the Andrew platform. In keeping with Andrew's original schedule, first oil from Cyrus was to flow in early 1997 soon after the platform had come on stream.

In February 1994, Cyrus received sanction along with Andrew. With a target cost of £24 million plus £1.8 million unallocated provision, the development plan was based upon a subsea bundle connecting Cyrus' wells with Andrew. The bundle would convey produced fluids from the smaller field to the platform for processing, and also carry from the platform gas for gas lift, chemical injection, plus hydraulic and electrical control signals for the subsea wells.

Following sanction, BP – the sole licensee in the block – went out for competitive tender for the work, taking a leaf from Andrew's book by applying Minimum Conditions of Satisfaction as part of the selection process. Subsea specialist Rockwater was successful in securing the contract for the Cyrus work in April 1994, entering into an alliance with BP under a 50-50 gainshare agreement.

'At the very beginning of the project we set out our new business targets for Cyrus,' says Ewan Drummond, BP's project manager. Having transferred from the Andrew team where he had been involved from predevelopment stage onwards to become budget responsibility officer for installation, Drummond was well versed with BP's determination to move away from the 'business as usual' approach. 'The first monthly report for Cyrus set a stretched target of £19 million for the development, aiming for an ambitious £5 million cost reduction. We also called for the bundle to be installed in 1995 – a year earlier than first planned – in order to minimise congestion in the area at the time of Andrew's installation. And in conjunction with these aims, we established our 'essential behaviours' – the way we would work together to deliver the business result.'

Beneath the waves
Cyrus

Cyrus bundle towhead housing
Andrew's subsea isolation valves.

The essential behaviours he refers to were based on the premise that all problems arising would be dealt with as Cyrus problems rather than individual company problems, and would be resolved in a spirit of openness and co-operation. Closely reflecting the Andrew working approach, the project also adopted the freedom to challenge standing solutions, inviting well-reasoned changes and innovation with the aim of continuously improving the final outcome for Cyrus.

'We established our 'essential behaviours' – the way we would work together to deliver the business result'

Ewan Drummond
Cyrus project manager BP

Rockwater's works contract to design, procure and install bundle, towheads and manifold, accounted for two thirds of the target cost. The remainder, some £8 million, was earmarked for control system, subsea trees, well workover package and engineering. As part of the Brown & Root group, Rockwater had trading agreements with its sister companies, bringing into the project Brown & Root's engineering skills for the specification of the overall control system, while BARMAC at Nigg fabricated the towhead and manifold; the bundle and towheads were designed by Rockwater, and would be built at the company's Wester fabrication site at Wick. Decisions on key suppliers to the project were taken jointly by BP and Rockwater as managers of the Cyrus alliance.

'Although Cyrus was a smaller job than Andrew the combination of tight schedule and low target cost presented real challenges,' notes Sandy Dickson of Rockwater, deputy project manager. 'In general subsea projects display a high risk of overrunning their budgets, mainly due to inefficient control of the interfaces between client, contractors and suppliers. On Cyrus we were given the freedom – and the trust – to run the project, eliminating the client as a go-between, which eased the interactions between the companies involved. There was no longer the imposition of having to seek permission from layers of unnecessary management for every decision.'

Similar to Andrew, the project dispensed with duplication – BP had no representative in Rockwater's Aberdeen project office; functional specifications were widely used – a typical case was that of the subsea control system, for which Kvaerner FSSL carried out detailed design; and enrolment of suppliers played a key role in ensuring timely and complete deliveries.

Engineering innovation made a major impact on the Cyrus target cost. The development was centred on the 6.6km long bundle connecting Cyrus with the Andrew platform, the first occasion BP had opted for this style of subsea technology. Brown & Root's designers had already proposed that the towhead structure for the bundle could house Andrew's SSIVs, removing a 60t subsea structure from the plan. Now further innovations came forward from the Cyrus team which drove down the cost of the subsea development still more.

Contained within a 28in diameter carrier pipe, the bundle consists of a 10in production pipeline, 4in gas lift line, 2in service line, plus electrical cables and hydraulic tubing. At the platform end the towhead structure acts as the connection point for the export pipelines leaving the platform and for the multiple lines running to Cyrus; at the opposite end, the Cyrus manifold structure houses connections and control system for the two subsea wells.

'An early breakthrough came as the result of a challenge to the materials for the Cyrus production line,' recounts Drummond. 'Instead of using costly super duplex stainless steel to manufacture the line, Rockwater proposed the duty could be met by a carbon steel pipe, internally clad with a stainless steel liner which was expanded to bond mechanically with the outer pipe. This would be new technology for the North Sea, and there was some concern at first. But by a team effort – including research and testing by the supplier Buttings in Germany – we concluded it was the best solution. The outcome was a net saving of £900,000 – it set us off to a great start in getting below the target cost.'

Fabrication of the bundle at Wick also saw Cyrus break new ground. Although longer bundles had been produced before, these had been fabricated by joining together shorter lengths; for Cyrus the bundle would be fabricated in one single piece, the longest yet manufactured. 'To build the bundle in one piece required the construction track – and the site – to be extended by half a kilometre,' says Dickson. 'But we had planned for this investment, knowing that it would increase fabrication efficiency with overall cost advantages for the project. Retaining flexibility during fabrication was the key.'

That flexibility was further reinforced by the decision to install electrical and hydraulic components separately within the bundle. The normal practice of combining these into a single 6.6km umbilical could create handling problems at

Cross section of Cyrus bundle.

Beneath the waves
Cyrus

'There was plenty of old baggage between us. But this was a new game and we had to get rid of that baggage'

Sandy Dickson
Cyrus project manager Rockwater

Beneath the waves
Cyrus

Fabrication of 6.6km long bundle in one piece required extension of the construction track at Wick.

site and entailed extra manufacturing costs. Instead, the nine coated stainless steel tubes for hydraulic fluids and chemical injection, plus four electrical signal cables, were kept as separate components and installed in the bundle individually. Capital cost reduction of around £100,000 was accompanied by significant improvements in site productivity.

Fabrication began in December 1994, with the towhead and manifold arriving at Wick early the next year in readiness for the tow to the field in May 1995. 'Installation went very well,' says Dickson. 'No divers were involved and it was the first bundle installed without seabed manoeuvring. The underlying reason for the success was that we had been able to delegate responsibility for each phase of the project to the best man for the job from the outset. Helping to set project targets and then delivering against these creates ownership and at the same time enables people to develop.'

Once installed, the pipelines and subsea components required interconnection to complete the system, tasks which called for diving support. Under the initial plan, installing the connecting spool pieces for Andrew's pipelines was to be carried out by Allseas, while all Cyrus related spools would be installed by Rockwater. 'There appeared the likelihood that two diving support vessels working in the area would create congestion, and moreover would lead to duplication of effort,' explains Brown & Root's Mike McSherry, who was instrumental in forging the diving alliance. As a result, BP proposed in early 1995 that all diving work tie-in should be merged into a single new contract, performed under a diving alliance between Rockwater, Allseas and the Andrew alliance.

Though attractive in theory, forming the alliance was less than smooth in practice. 'Bringing together two contractors which traditionally have been rivals was not easy to begin with,' admits Allseas' Peter Olden. 'Trust was needed for us to consider close co-operation – BP was a catalyst in making this happen.' Sandy Dickson agrees. 'There was plenty of old baggage between us. But this was a new game, and we had to get rid of that baggage.'

The diving alliance scope, covering all tie-ins around the platform and at the Brae and CATS pipelines, plus testing and commissioning of the system, was valued at £7.1 million, involving some 40 spool connections. Rather than wait until the platform was first installed – the more usual practice – the diving alliance went to work early in March 1996 to take advantage of having access to the open sea. 'We've learned from experience that when there's a lot of activity occurring in the field, the subsea work is normally told to wait as it's viewed as one of the less costly contracts for the project. But delays caused by such clashes incur extra costs unnecessarily – we were determined to avoid this.'

The strategy paid off, providing Rockwater's vessels *Semi 2* and *Rockwater 1* with greater operating flexibility. Other preparations also contributed to reducing the time offshore. During the Cyrus installation a year before, all Andrew pipelines and structures had also been carefully surveyed to determine the precise length of spools required, permitting onshore prefabrication and testing rather than manufacturing the spools on deck offshore.

By the time of platform installation, the only subsea work remaining was as planned – the final tie-in spools to the platform's risers, plus testing and commissioning. The diving alliance had come in over £1 million below budget.

'Looking back over the Cyrus project, we are very proud of the achievement,' says BP's Ewan Drummond. 'We almost made the ambitious £19 million target, coming in at just over £20 million – a reduction of over twenty percent from sanction budget, similar to the larger Andrew project. Much of the success stems from maintaining our flexibility – it shows that the traditional way of 'plan the work, then work the plan' is not necessarily the best.'

'Cyrus is one of the most successful jobs undertaken by Rockwater,' adds Dickson. 'We've progressed our team, our technology and made money. Like Andrew, it has all been about grasping opportunities when they arise.'

Cyrus bundle and towhead being pulled out to sea in May 1995. The project achieved a reduction in expenditure of over twenty percent compared with the sanctioned budget.

Total acquisition

'In effect we were questioning all the steps in the supply chain – it was a fundamental shift away from normal practice'

Norman Brown
Supplier alliance manager BP

Andrew's resolve to cultivate new working relationships as catalysts for cost reduction was not confined to the eight alliance members. From the earliest presanction days there was general recognition that, as with all North Sea developments, the supply of equipment packages and materials would have a significant influence on the project's economic results. That influence would come not only from the capital cost of purchasing, but also from the wider array of procurement-related activities – design, quality assurance, supplier performance and delivery. Late delivery of incomplete products to the fabrication yards, most critically for topsides construction, carried the potential to cause delays and major cost overruns, along with a negative impact on Andrew's overall schedule.

Together, BP and Brown & Root, as first members of the alliance and responsible for procurement, took the view that an innovative approach to equipment and materials acquisition was necessary if the shortcomings of 'business as usual' were not to creep in and steer the project away from its goal of achieving success on all fronts. A strategy was required which would break down old antagonisms between client, contractor and suppliers, enrolling all participants in a wider Andrew team with the shared objective of meeting the project's demanding targets.

Supplier alliance manager Norman Brown of BP and Brown & Root's materials manager Peter Jessup joined forces to lead an initiative which was to set an industry benchmark in the acquisition of equipment and materials for an offshore development.

'Our overall aim was to create a supply environment which could achieve cost reduction without compromising safety or quality, and which would not eat into suppliers' profits,' explains Norman Brown. 'In the same way that the alliance contractors had committed to Andrew's success, we were seeking to enlist the support of suppliers by painting a clear picture of the project's targets and encouraging them to contribute their skills, to develop ownership in the project with a chance to enhance their company's profitability. At the same time we were also looking at procurement activities directly in our control; technical specifications, expediting and inspection featured prominently. In effect we were questioning all the steps in the supply chain – it was a fundamental shift away from normal practice.'

Peter Jessup reinforces this view. 'Traditionally when selecting suppliers we would judge on lowest price, technical acceptability, and shortest delivery; get the order placed, perhaps without full understanding of its detail; then load the suppliers with expediters and inspectors to drive it along. But you have to ask

Fabrication of production separators.

whether this method really achieved the required end result. For Andrew we decided to dismantle the old approach and concentrate instead on best value.'

Guiding the formulation of the best value strategy was the focus on total acquisition cost, rather than on suppliers' bid prices. Total acquisition cost is significantly different in that it includes not only the equipment purchase cost but also the associated expenditure incurred by the design contractor in pursuing and achieving the required quality and delivery date. Furthermore, it takes account of the potential influence the equipment can have on fabrication yard costs – the degree of completion of the package and its likely effect on commissioning.

In early 1993, the estimated cost for acquiring Andrew's topsides equipment and materials stood at £72 million. By applying the new approach to procurement, the project set itself a challenge to reduce this figure by 30%.

Identifying the characterising elements of the traditional procurement process was a first step towards change. Accompanying the 'business as usual' method for supplier selection described by Jessup, the offshore industry had historically relied on certain standard methods in its dealings with suppliers. Elaborate prescriptive specifications were used by clients and major contractors with a 'we know best' attitude to obtaining equipment packages. Large and detailed volumes of duplicated documentation were demanded from suppliers as proof of their actions, often accumulated in readiness for any later contractual conflict and indicating a

> **Topsides equipment and materials**
> Procurement strategy
>
> **Objectives:**
>
> Support the design and fabrication schedules
>
> Develop new non-adversarial relationships with suppliers
>
> Reduce total acquisition costs of products compared with previous projects
>
> Maximise supplier contribution
>
> Comply with requirements of European Community Utilities Directive

degree of inherent mistrust between the parties. Teams of field expediters and inspectors would be employed to check continuously on both supplier adherence to the specifications and progress toward delivery dates. Late deliveries of incomplete packages with long punch lists of outstanding work were commonplace – an indictment on the failings of the procurement approach.

'There's a well known saying which defines insanity as doing the same thing over and over again and expecting a different result,' Brown points out. 'Unfortunately that's what the industry had been doing for years in its interaction with suppliers; as clients we had been too arrogant in our approach. Then, when performance fell short of the mark, everyone took up opposing positions. We were determined to avoid this on Andrew.'

The project based its procurement strategy on treating suppliers as team members, first providing them with a full understanding of Andrew's objectives, encouraging them to accept responsibility for their part in achieving those goals, and then supporting suppliers in their efforts rather than adopting a threatening stance, particularly when manufacturing problems arose.

The building blocks of Andrew's philosophy for equipment and materials supply were laid out clearly in 'user friendly' enquiry packages. Prescription by the client was out; instead functional specifications would be issued which would request fit-for-purpose products, inviting suppliers to contribute their specialist knowledge by offering standard equipment and by proposing innovations. 'The North Sea has a reputation for overspecifying on equipment needs,' notes Jessup. 'The idea behind the functional specifications was to strip out all the 'nice-to-have bells and whistles' which serve only to push up the price.'

Documentation was a key target, notorious for consuming tens of thousands of manhours in its preparation, review and acceptance. Suppliers are normally called on to submit copious volumes of paperwork from the bid stage onward, much of which is superfluous to the project's practical needs. Detailed calculations for each and every component in a package, and data generated during manufacture and testing, could equally well reside with the supplier on the understanding that this would be available if required. Certification data was also minimised in conjunction with Lloyd's Register. To this end, the target for documentation to be submitted and reviewed by the project was set 40% below normal levels for a project of Andrew's size.

A radical departure came with the proposal to eliminate field expediting and minimise inspection, entrusting suppliers to perform to the same quality standards but under a policy of self-regulation. 'There was a widespread perception that the only reason a quality product was normally achieved was due to constant policing by the project,' observes Brown. 'We decided to move away from this and trust the suppliers to carry out their work in a mature and responsible fashion. There was some resistance to this at first – everyone had their stories about suppliers of course. But we nonetheless made the commitment not to intervene all the time, but be ready in support if problems occurred.'

Though aware that the overall strategy encompassed a degree of risk by virtue of the fact that it had not before been put into practice to this extent, the project was to receive encouragement for its pioneering moves when the UK offshore industry's Cost Reduction Initiative for the New Era (CRINE) announced its goals for making the sector more competitive on the world stage. The close similarities with Andrew's formula for pursuing success injected added confidence into the team. As an added backdrop, the project was one of the first offshore developments coming into action under the European Union's new Utilities Directive on procurement.

Underpinning the key building blocks was the firm intent to work with suppliers in a more open and honest fashion, developing a closer understanding of their cost drivers while making them aware of Andrew's fabrication schedule. Prior to the issue of tenders, all prospective suppliers were issued with information packs about the project, the alliance and the importance of changing behaviour as an essential ingredient in the North Sea industry's continuing survival, emphasised and reinforced by presentation and workshop sessions with all suppliers.

'Bid evaluation was also processed differently,' says Jessup. 'For each package we had developed a set of predetermined award criteria to reflect 'best value' which was established before bids were opened. We were no longer simply seeking the lowest price and shortest delivery, but value and delivery which suited Andrew's schedule, plus technical suitability for integration into the platform over its lifetime. Equally important was a demonstration of commitment to and alignment with Andrew's goals, an ability to manage and control the work, and potential to provide added value through innovation.'

The project team was structured to match the new procurement strategy. Package teams of five people were set up, led by engineers backed up by quality assurance, safety, operations and purchasing specialists – previously these disciplines had worked independently, missing the advantages of cross-questioning and the building of team ownership. Package teams were enrolled into the procurement philosophy and coached throughout its implementation, taking the leading role in selecting suppliers and seeing the package through to delivery. Feedback from the teams was used to improve the process.

An important intermediate step was included in the supplier selection process, whereby a prime bidder was first identified through the best value criteria. Working with the prime bidder, the package team would then optimise the

'The idea behind the functional specifications was to strip out all the 'nice-to-have bells and whistles' which serve only to push up the price'

Peter Jessup
Materials manager Brown & Root

Topsides equipment and materials
Procurement process

Target 30% reduction in total cost of topsides equipment and materials acquisition by:

Issue of functional specifications to secure fit-for-purpose products

Use of suppliers' standard equipment

Reduction in supplier documentation submitted for approval

Encouragement of supplier contribution and alignment to Andrew's goals

Issue of user-friendly enquiry packages to suppliers

Elimination of items which add cost but not value

Minimum field expediting and inspection

Total acquisition

equipment package. Items which added cost but not value were challenged, while full understanding of fit-for-purpose standard products and innovative proposals were pursued. Suppliers' profit margins were maintained, with the potential to increase profits further if costs to the project were reduced. 'The purpose of the optimisation process was to ensure both sides had clarity on what was included and what was expected of them,' adds Jessup. 'This was essential if the policy of self-regulation was to work correctly.'

He cites just a few of the many examples where bid optimisation paid off for the project. Savings were made by further streamlining standard products in the air compressor package from Ingersoll-Rand, while the manufacturer maintained its profit margin; welded rather than seamless titanium tubulars were proposed by Hans Leffer for shell and tube heat exchangers, netting a saving of £250,000; and the elimination of a string test for the main power generators supplied by European Gas Turbines reduced delivery time and provided savings of over £400,000.

Optimisation also provided much greater confidence about costs and delivery. By the time of the sanction estimate submission, suppliers of the fifteen major packages had been identified – together these accounted for over half of the topsides equipment and materials budget – enabling the project to incorporate accurate prices into Andrew's target cost rather than rely on historical trends. At sanction in February 1994, the procurement strategy had already proved highly effective in reducing the equipment and materials budget for the integrated deck by over 20% to £56 million.

According to Brown, alongside the focus on cost reduction, the other primary objectives of the procurement strategy were to determine and achieve realistic delivery dates to support the fabrication schedule. 'The common approach is to set notional delivery dates for equipment packages early in the project and then to

Assembly of one of the platform's three main power generators.

apply a big expediting effort to ensure these are met. If they should be late, the process of claiming variation orders is all too readily resorted to. But does the topsides fabricator really need them then? For Andrew we had a significant advantage in this respect by having the topsides fabricator, TJB, in the alliance to set realistic field need dates for the packages. Topsides construction was to be commissioning-led – the package deliveries were set to match the commissioning programme.'

Supplier response

The Andrew supplier initiative was by no means solely a device for driving down costs at the front end of the project. The momentum generated by the bid selection process now had to be maintained – by the suppliers and package teams to ensure quality and delivery dates were met, and by the alliance in addressing suppliers' problems and jointly finding solutions which would keep the schedule on track. Enrolment and coaching retained a high profile. Visits by Andrew's project managers and package engineers to manufacturing sites helped update suppliers on the project's progress, consciously preventing the sense of isolation which can mount among vendors during the months required to fulfil contracts. Another link came through distribution of the project's newsletter to all suppliers, acting as a further status update. Suppliers were also invited to acknowledgement days at the topsides fabrication yard in Teesside, both to give feedback on the acquisition process through brainstorming sessions, and in due course to see their equipment installed in the integrated deck – a seemingly simple gesture and yet for the majority of suppliers, particularly for smaller manufacturers, the first opportunity offered to them to develop a better appreciation of their equipment in the context of an offshore platform.

'Andrew exhibited high ideals in its early prequalification meetings, but we suspected that in time matters would revert to traditional business practices,' recalls Arthur Cuss, project co-ordinator for Sulzer, supplier of the platform's export and injection gas compressor trains. 'But not so. The project held true to its intentions and allowed us to work in our own way – less documentation, the use of vendor standards, and minimal inspection helped our production teams. Less interference saves manhours and avoids potential acrimony at the interfaces – we felt part of the project, enjoyed the atmosphere and consider it to be a significant success both for our customer and our company.'

Functional specifications for the gas compressors – one of Andrew's largest packages, valued around £9 million – permitted Sulzer to provide standard equipment and also made room for innovation. Dry gas seals used in the compressors operate at a pressure differential of 280 bar, the highest pressure

'Andrew exhibited high ideals in its early prequalification meetings, but we suspected that in time matters would revert to traditional business practices. But not so'

Arthur Cuss
Project co-ordinator Sulzer

'The approach to procurement was something of a jolt to the industry when we first announced our intention to work this way. But the results speak for themselves'

Norman Brown
Supplier alliance manager BP

Total acquisition
Supplier response

Installation of gas compressors into integrated deck, twelve months before sailaway.

application thus far for the technology and a first in the North Sea. 'Innovations were taken onboard very early due to the intensive bid optimisation process on Andrew,' adds Cuss. 'As a result scope and costs were much more clearly defined than usual. We experienced very little growth in the contract compared with conventional projects.'

As part of the positive approach to supplier relations, the alliance had also promised to assist vendors constructively with problems which would inevitably occur. That commitment was put to the test when Sulzer found itself confronted with the dilemma of two major customers simultaneously placing demands on its testbed facilities. Gordon Ratcliffe, divisional director for Sulzer, explains.

'In 1994 we had won two important compressor contracts around the same time, both on tight delivery programmes – for the Andrew alliance and for Shell Expro's Pelican project. At an early stage in buying critical components it became clear that nozzle forgings for all barrel casings would not be available until much later than scheduled. No way could be found to shorten the delivery. The conclusion was that both projects would suffer the same knock-on effect, bringing the Pelican and Andrew compressor sets to the Sulzer testbed in Switzerland at the same time, and one month later than planned. The conclusion was irrefutable: there would be only one testing slot. Something had to give.'

The impact of large compressor packages arriving late for installation into integrated decks presented no small threat to project schedules. A typical course of action for the package supplier would be to announce the delay to both customers and wait to see which one 'shouted the loudest'. This would then be followed by two separate wars of attrition with Sulzer and 'nine months of hell' for the production team. Instead, Sulzer decided to try out the new behaviour on offer from the Andrew alliance, and approach the Pelican project which had also espoused a more 'vendor friendly' attitude.

'The idea was to get the two project managers together to put their cards on the table, to see whether float remained in their overall schedules rather than focus only on the compressor delivery dates,' recounts Ratcliffe. 'The vision of two clients at the same table was ridiculed at first within Sulzer. But the outcome was quite surprising.'

Both clients reacted quickly. The Pelican team stated that their schedule was too far advanced to accommodate the delay; but a telephone call from Pelican to Andrew resolved the issue. The detailed fabrication and commissioning plan drawn up by the alliance revealed that Sulzer could be allowed an extra month-long window on delivery to Teesside, presenting Pelican with the first testbed slot to attain its planned delivery. Sulzer's response resulted in the tested Andrew compressor trains arriving at the fabrication yard at the beginning of the new delivery window in April 1995. Within a week of arrival the machines were installed in the integrated deck, twelve months before sailaway.

The move away from old behavioural responses did not come without effort for the alliance team, as Norman Brown observes. 'When the going got tough it would have been easy to revert to traditional stances. On one occasion we went to visit a key supplier – eight weeks from delivery and the factory looked an utter shambles to us. If we were buying a standard product, where were the production lines, the control systems? But this was only *our* perception – we didn't know how to run their business. In reality the job was under close control and we had the assurance of the managing director that the schedule would be met – and it was. On such occasions the faith in our own philosophy was seriously tested.'

While not all manufacturing problems found relatively straightforward solutions, the alliance did endeavour to co-operate with suppliers as members of the wider Andrew team. A case in point concerned the supply of electrical and instrument cables from BICC. In keeping with the alliance's desire to minimise client inspection, BICC's suggestion that no site inspection would be necessary – the cables would already be certified by Lloyd's Register – was accepted by the project.

'The cables were tested and passed in the factory in the normal way, and also passed a further electrical test while still on their drums when they arrived in Teesside,' relates BICC's Harry Roberts. 'But when the cables were being installed a fault was found in some of the instrument cable – by its nature the fault would not have been picked up during any factory inspections nor by the electrical tests which were carried out.'

'On such occasions the faith in our own philosophy was seriously tested'

Norman Brown
Supplier alliance manager BP

Total acquisition
Supplier response

'We have never experienced such assistance on a project before; we genuinely felt we were part of the team'

Harry Roberts
BICC

The problem was swiftly investigated by BICC, determining that the fault was limited to only a few kilometres of cable in an order totalling several hundred kilometres. Within two days, 5km of new cable had been manufactured at the supplier's own expense, halting other orders to accommodate Andrew – disappointingly only to discover that the problem had reappeared. 'We were amazed by the Andrew team's response,' says Roberts. 'They came forward with suggestions and practical assistance, not the tradition of charges for downtime and additional work. Together we discovered the problem was being caused by a particular feature of the cable laying process and modified this. We took the decision to take no risks by scrapping all the cable of this type, and within three weeks had manufactured some 20km of replacement cable. The corrective work entailed significant added cost for BICC.'

Unfortunately much of the faulty cable had already been installed in the integrated deck and had to be pulled out for the replacement exercise. Contractually, the alliance could have sought compensation from BICC, but instead took the view that the supplier had performed in the spirit of the alliance by acting promptly to solve the problem without being forced into decisions, thereby avoiding delays to construction. 'We have never experienced this on a project before, we genuinely felt we were part of the team,' states Roberts. 'Not only have we been treated very fairly, we have been helped to overcome an obscure manufacturing problem, and our workforce at all levels has benefited enormously from the involvement with Andrew. The shop floor now brings both problems and suggestions forward, adding to our knowledge and advancing the company's competitiveness.'

Chemical injection package.

Positive supplier response also featured in another case where faulty materials caused outfitting rework to the integrated deck. Proactive safety inspections at the Teesside yard on critical pipeline components revealed that some super duplex stainless steel pipe fittings were substandard. The fittings, a small portion of a large order placed with Avesta and manufactured by a subsupplier in Italy, were found to be defective due to a faulty door on the heat treatment furnace. The suppliers accepted responsibility, corrected the manufacturing problem, and resupplied at their own cost. As Brown points out, the traditional reflex response would have been to fill the shortfall by ordering elsewhere, probably ordering extra to be on the safe side. By attending to the problem and continuing with the same manufacturer, additional costs of reordering were avoided.

'There was a spin off to the problem too,' he adds. 'In talking to the suppliers we learned that our ordering method was causing them to manufacture in uneconomic quantities due to the project's computerised material take off system – this had essentially outstripped manufacturing capability. We were wrong to assume that we understood their way of working, and we were in effect costing them and the project money. We set up improved delivery commitments as a result – it taught us that the procurement enrolment process needs to include the major subsuppliers too.'

Reception for Andrew's innovative procurement process among the project's suppliers – over 75% of materials and equipment were purchased from the United Kingdom – was generally positive, with a strong preference being expressed for the co-operative working of the alliance. Naturally with such a broad spectrum of interests and contract sizes, coupled with the uncertainties of a cultural shift, not all suppliers felt every aspect of the strategy had been totally successful.

Kvaerner FSSL, in producing the industry's first platform control system which fully integrates all systems – process control, fire and gas, emergency shutdown and subsea included – considers changes to the design became more numerous than anticipated. 'Because our system interfaced with almost everything on the platform, it was subjected to change from a number of sources,' explains Coleen Eardley, the company's general manager of computer operations. 'Early involvement of the control system vendor is critical to the smooth running of the project, but a more focused assessment of that involvement would have been beneficial in dealing with the change cycle. However, we did come forward with a solution to the changes which were impacting us by delivering our equipment to Teesside in two phases to match the construction programme. In this respect we received the full support of the Andrew team, and were always able to trust that the commercial outcome would be equitable.'

Weir Pumps, which supplied the majority of Andrew's large pump packages valued at some £3 million, was also broadly impressed, says senior design engineer Lindsay Maxwell. 'After contract award, members of the Andrew team came to the factory for an induction meeting. This was not like the normal confrontational

Top: Central control room

Above: One of the platform's main oil line pumps.

Total acquisition
Supplier response

'It was something of a cultural shock when instead of laying down the law the Andrew team asked what they could do for us'

Lindsay Maxwell
Senior design engineer Weir Pumps

kick-off meetings – in fact it was something of a cultural shock when instead of laying down the law they asked what they could do for us. The enthusiasm brushed off on us all.'

In progressing its contract, Weir Pumps noted that in most respects Andrew's ideals were achieved – functional specifications, reduced documentation, less changes and a receptiveness to new ideas; group brainstorming sessions led to two fire pumps being installed and commissioned in their caissons entirely onshore. But in some cases delivery dates were missed by a few weeks. 'A degree of expediting would still seem necessary in these circumstances,' notes Maxwell. 'But not as much as in the past; a balance between the two would be better.'

Chemical injection package supplier Vanpipe Process Systems takes a slightly different view. 'Minimising expediting and inspection was a positive move forward,' comments director Stephen Harding. 'We were allowed to work in our own way without interference from client or contractors – this helped keep manhours down and we enjoyed the project more. If there is a criticism it is that we found the supplier selection process too drawn out, but the fit-for-purpose specifications were very effective in driving out costs on the package.'

Procurement payoff

Prominent among observations made by suppliers in providing feedback to the alliance was the clear agreement that Andrew's procurement strategy was a resounding success, with many companies now taking the philosophy forward to influence other offshore projects. For the alliance, that success can be measured by the achievement of its target to reduce total acquisition cost by 30%.

'The outturn capital cost for topsides equipment and materials totalled £52 million, some £20 million less than the original estimate,' declares Norman Brown. 'On top of this, reductions in procurement, documentation and transportation costs saved a further £6 million, giving a 36% overall decrease compared with the 'business as usual' figure, beating the 30% target. All packages were delivered to the topsides fabrication yard such that construction milestones were all met – there were late deliveries but nothing impacted the overall schedule.'

By closely supporting the fabrication effort, the supplier initiative contributed in a highly visible way to Andrew's revolutionary onshore completion strategy, discarding the old image of supplier unreliability being the cause of costly construction delays. In the meeting of all fabrication milestones, over 98% of the 240 or so topsides purchase orders were delivered earlier than field need dates. About half of all orders were delivered on specified contractual dates, the bulk of the remainder arriving within four weeks without affecting construction schedules. 'Only fourteen purchase orders were delivered with minor punchlists for vendors to complete at site at their cost,' adds Brown. 'The degree of completion of the packages was a major improvement over previous projects. The alliance had no contractual claims to issue on Andrew.'

In addition to the direct reduction of equipment and material costs, the other £6 million savings which Brown refers to were secured throughout the procurement process. Manhours expended by Brown & Root in performing the procurement function were cut by over 20% to around 143,000 – a saving of £1.5 million compared with a traditional project of Andrew's size. Key contributors were the halving of field inspection and the elimination of field expediting. Reduced transportation costs – achieved under a risk and reward contract with the freight forwarding company LV Shipping – and a decrease in traffic manhours, notched up further savings of £725,000.

Clear definition of suppliers' workscope in support of the onshore commissioning programme, plus the completion of packages at the vendors' works, led to over £500,000 being cut from the supplier commissioning budget, a 25% reduction.

The alliance's determination to minimise supplier documentation submitted to the project yielded outstanding results, as Peter Jessup points out. 'Comparing Andrew's 10,000t topsides with platforms of a similar size shows a remarkable fall in the volume of paperwork. Some platforms in the past – including those for BP – have run up as much as 50,000 submitted documents; Andrew totalled 6,900. For the largest packages we managed to bring documents down to a single volume, and for some purchase orders achieved a single data sheet. Even compared to the most recent integrated deck of this size, documentation has been reduced by 75%. That's equivalent to a saving of some £3.3 million in manhours, and far exceeds our original target of beating 'business as usual' documentation by 40%.'

The success of Andrew's approach to equipment and materials procurement is attributed by both Brown and Jessup to careful planning and teamwork in an open and honest environment. 'It was something of a jolt to the industry when we announced our intention to work this way,' reflects Norman Brown. 'But the results speak for themselves, proving that safe, quality products, completed to agreed specifications, can be delivered on time with minimum intervention from the client – and can bring significant cost benefits to the project.'

Topsides equipment and materials

Total acquisition results:

Procurement manhours reduced overall by 21.5% including:

Purchasing	20%
Field expediting	100%
Field inspection	52%
Engineering	0.5%
Manhour cost savings	£1.5m

75% reduction in supplier documentation

98% of all purchase orders delivered before fabrication need dates

No contractual claims issued

Total acquisition cost reduced by £26 million (36% reduction) compared to 'business as usual' estimate

Safety without compromise

Concurrent with the development of Andrew's cost reducing initiatives, the project was required to address another all encompassing change, one with far reaching effects for the alliance and entire offshore industry. A radical overhaul of legislation governing the UK's offshore safety regime was under way, moving to a significantly different philosophy centred on goal-setting regulations. The previous system of extensive prescriptive rules controlling the design and operation of offshore installations was being phased out and replaced by a more modern risk-based approach to safety, a transition demanding a cultural adjustment across the industry.

At the heart of the new regime, every operating oil company is required to demonstrate its safety management system to the industry's newly appointed regulator, the Offshore Safety Division of the Health & Safety Executive (HSE). As a primary component of the safety management system, a company is legally obliged to produce design and operational safety cases for each new and existing offshore installation, to be accepted by HSE. The safety case must show that risks from major hazards have been evaluated and measures taken to reduce those risks to as low a level as is reasonably practicable.

With safety case legislation entering the statute books in May 1993, Andrew became a front runner for the industry, as the project's health, safety and environment team leader John Allinson of BP explains.

'The schedule for Andrew meant it would become the first fixed manned platform in the UK to require a design safety case, and additionally would be the first installation to move through all stages of the safety case process which includes operations. This presented very real challenges for the team as there were no previous references for the new approach – we had to interpret the legislation and generate new ideas. We were also aware of further legislation that was very likely to come into effect during the design and construction period and had to take account of this in advance. It was a time of learning for us all.'

But would there be a fundamental conflict for Andrew? How could the project's commitment to reducing costs across the board be reconciled with improving safety wherever possible?

'Those two goals were never in competition,' Allinson asserts. 'Safety has always assumed paramount importance on all BP projects and that was absolutely the case for Andrew too. The full support of project management, and BP and its partners was always behind safety. There was no possibility of compromise.'

'Safety has always assumed paramount importance on all BP projects. There was no possibility of compromise'

John Allinson
Health, safety and environment
team leader BP

Indeed Andrew was destined to prove that cost reduction and improved safety can go hand-in-hand, a practical demonstration justifying the industry adage that cost effective business is also safer business.

From the presanction phase of the project, the Andrew team invited close co-operation with both the certifying authority Lloyd's Register and HSE. 'Continuous involvement with Lloyd's surveyors throughout design and construction enabled the feasibility – and acceptability – of technical and safety proposals to be discussed in detail,' recounts David Cummergen, Lloyd's Register's project manager for Andrew. 'This was particularly relevant in light of the changing regulatory regime with older rules phasing out and members of the project team coming up with new ideas for safety. The presence of the certifying authority in the team provided an impartial forum for sounding out their proposals.'

However, initial concern was expressed by HSE over the alliance's intention to move away from the traditional practice of continuous monitoring and supervision of contractors and suppliers by client representatives. Andrew's stated goal of eliminating man-for-man marking and the transfer of responsibility to each of the alliance contractors was viewed by HSE as a 'dilution of BP's responsibility as duty holder', recalls Allinson.

A case in point was for the installation of Andrew's export pipelines, with the supervision of Allseas, as contractor to BP, coming into question. 'In the past we would have specified and closely monitored all work by contractors,' Allinson observes. 'But now we were passing responsibility to them as alliance members, in the process requesting submission of their own plans for safety management. It was a topic of some debate, but in due course HSE accepted that high safety standards would be maintained – they audited the pipelaying operation onboard *Lorelay* and were impressed by the degree of ownership and pride taken in the work. Safety and quality standards were just as good without client overseers.'

Platform design and fabrication commanded critical attention from the safety team and HSE. Though the move to the new safety culture and formal safety assessments was a transitional process, Andrew's climate for openly challenging established design procedures paved the way for the goal-setting philosophy to take hold as quickly as possible. In response, safety issues raised by the design team reached ten times the number associated with previous prescriptive regulation. 'If it had to do with safety, it needed an answer,' says Allinson.

Major effort was dedicated to topsides layout and blast loading, with the temporary refuge, now statutorily required, being located in the integrated deck below the accommodation module. Safety within the accommodation module was the focus of extensive studies, with one design challenge giving rise to the exclusion of fire water sprinklers in the module's cabins. By formal safety assessment,

Allseas pipelay vessel *Lorelay*.

Safety without compromise

supported by quantitative risk analysis and full scale trials, the team was able to demonstrate to HSE that the platform's fire risk reduction measures, rapid detection of smoke and fire, plus extensive passive fire protection, provided inherently safer conditions in the living quarters.

Package suppliers were not excluded from the risk assessment approach. Whereas in the past a supplier's perception of the safety assessments made by the main design contractor was often confined to a list of additional cost and schedule impacts for the package, Andrew's suppliers were involved in the assessment process. This provided greater insight of the safety implications for package suppliers in relation to platform operations.

While the early inclusion of integrated deck fabricator TJB into the design team proved very effective in identifying ways to reduce the cost of construction, the initiative also had an equally positive effect on improving safety for the 650-strong workforce at the Teesside yard.

'On traditional contracts we have had to build integrated decks to match an already existing design,' states Brian Hall, TJB's safety and training manager. 'Without the opportunity to influence the design and resulting build method, the fabricator is left to deal with inherent construction risks. On Andrew we were given the chance to reduce these risks by incorporating our experience into the design.'

Input to design came on both the grand scale and detailed levels to make fabrication easier and therefore safer. For the overall construction of the process-utilities deck, TJB proposed using the 'pancake' build method, whereby the topsides' three deck levels would be fabricated separately and in parallel, with major equipment then installed. The three levels would then be stacked one on another to form the integrated process-utilities deck, rather than the alternative of first constructing the entire 'box' and then proceeding to install equipment. The stacking strategy allowed each deck to be significantly completed while still at ground level, reducing risk to the workforce by enabling operations to be carried out from scaffolding erected on the ground to a working level of three metres, rather than rely on scaffolding hung from a deck eight metres above. A decrease in scaffolding and ladders reduced the number of accidents resulting from falls. Although TJB had employed the pancake method on previous projects, Andrew's procurement strategy delivered equipment and materials to the site on time, permitting a significant increase in deck outfitting at ground level, thus contributing to safer working and cutting down on the number of major equipment package lifts required.

The incidence of falls was further reduced by adopting a more efficient method for installing walkway gratings on the decks. The conventional approach entails five stages with gratings being lifted at least twice for welding and painting operations. With gratings removed, risks of falling are increased, while the activity itself leads to

manual handling accidents. For Andrew a simplified two-step procedure of laying gratings on steelwork already fully painted at ground level followed by fastening with thread-forming screws, avoided subsequent grating removal.

Another improvement to fabrication safety was achieved by modifying the design of in-deck diesel and water storage tanks. Past practice involved working in confined spaces for internal welding, blasting and painting – hazardous activities requiring high levels of safety control. For Andrew's deck, each tank was built as two separate assemblies, leaving off the base plate. Both components were fully painted prior to assembly as a complete tank, limiting internal work to essential field welds and minor remedial painting.

Together, these and other 'fabrication friendly' techniques including low preheat welding, had an impact on safety during the steelwork fabrication phase of Andrew's deck construction. The frequency rate of lost time incidents per million manhours worked (LTI) – an industry standard measure – was halved compared with the immediately preceding deck fabrication contract at the yard. Minor accidents dropped by 20%; severe falls from height were cut by more than 50%; manual handling accidents were reduced by 80%; and welding burns decreased by 75%. 'Simply saying we were working more safely was not enough,' Allinson points out. 'We needed to measure the improvement to show that Andrew's way of working was having a positive impact.'

Within the spectrum of safety improvements realised by the project, Andrew's onshore completions strategy stands perhaps as the most significant overall contributor. The radical move of eliminating an extensive offshore hookup and commissioning programme from the project – a direct result of the alliance's challenge to accepted practice – not only played a major part in the development's economic success, but elevated Andrew to new levels of safety achievement.

Complex construction and commissioning activities undertaken by large workforces in the offshore environment naturally carry a relatively high exposure to risk. By transferring the tasks to a safer location – onshore – many of the hazards associated with traditional offshore completion and logistics support operations disappear entirely. Those risks which do remain can often be lessened in severity, while the decrease in total manhours expended to achieve first oil inherently lowers individual exposure to hazards. Again the LTI frequency rate points to the advantages of onshore working. Two recent developments by BP involving new platforms in the North Sea notched up LTI rates of 10.9 and 11.3 during the offshore hookup and completions phases. For Andrew's equivalent onshore completion programme, LTI rate was more than halved at 5.3.

There was recognition that a number of the commissioning activities normally conducted offshore would be unfamiliar to the onshore construction workforce, leading the project to take extra measures to reinforce safety messages and

'On Andrew we were given the chance to reduce inherent construction risks by incorporating our experience into the design'

Brian Hall
Safety and training manager TJB

Safety without compromise

awareness. From the start of fabrication Andrew's management team had been proactive in ensuring the workforces at all sites were fully attuned to safety taking precedence over all other issues on the project. 'Never before has the client gathered the safety representatives together and instructed us that regardless of the pressures to get the job done, we were only to do it if it was safe,' remarks one TJB shop floor representative.

In addition to cutting accident rates, onshore completion at Teesside gave rise to other safety benefits. By commissioning and operating the platform's systems and living in the platform's accommodation module for three months before sailaway, the offshore operations team was able to identify and resolve problems in advance. A fully operational topsides enabled the team to become totally familiar with the platform's plant and control systems, conducting initial startups and testing emergency response plans in detail.

In April 1996, the operations team conducted a week-long series of onshore demonstrations to Lloyd's Register and HSE, proving full operation of platform systems and paying particular attention to safety management. Plans for emergency response to specific incidents derived from risk assessments were enacted through live exercises, among them firefighting, activation of fire and deluge systems, emergency control room operation and helicopter evacuation. So thorough were the demonstrations in covering all aspects of emergency preparedness and the competence of Andrew's asset team, that HSE's Aberdeen

Handover of the 'draft Certificate of Fitness' in Teesside, the first of its kind in the industry.

operations branch, responsible for monitoring offshore safety, declared its confidence by stating there would be no requirement for the regulator to witness repeat trials offshore. 'There will probably be no need for us to return to Andrew until the platform has been in operation for six months,' commented one HSE inspector.

Further endorsement came from HSE for Andrew's approach to the operations safety case, required now by law. Rather than produce a weighty volume of paper, the project implemented a computer-based system for accessing the safety case, incorporated into the proprietary Plant Manager software system which encompasses all platform operations.

'Andrew lives by its safety case,' emphasises offshore installation manager Owen Chappell. 'This is a live part of the platform operating system, providing a single source of up-to-date information which is easy to access and relevant to our day-to-day operations. It's a fundamental change from having a set of manuals sitting on the shelf which can sometimes discourage people from fully involving themselves in safety.'

'The safety case is also linked into Andrew's asset management system,' adds operations engineer Tim Dines. 'Eighty percent of all accidents are due to failure of management systems. We now have key management procedures linked to the safety case, which gives the team the right quality of information to make decisions – the tools to do the job.'

On 10 April, having successfully concluded the safety and operational demonstrations, Andrew was granted a 'draft Certificate of Fitness' by Lloyd's Register. The certificate, which listed a limited number of specific requirements which by their nature could only be performed offshore, was the first of its kind for the industry, signifying the certifying authority's confidence in the technical integrity of the installation and the competence of the asset team. Onshore completion also brought environmental benefits; full testing and operation of the platform's gas compressors at Teesside, together with all associated safety and utility systems, halved the time for produced gas to be flared to the atmosphere offshore during the initial start up period.

On 19 June, six weeks after leaving shore and having completed all work related to the limitations listed in the draft certificate, the platform received its full Certificate of Fitness for Production from Lloyd's Register. By now the alliance was secure in the knowledge that it had succeeded in attaining its goals of improving safety while at the same time markedly reducing capital development costs. First oil was about to flow six months early.

'Completion onshore has reduced risk and dramatically enhanced the safety, confidence and security of the offshore team,' BP project manager John Martin reflects. 'In conjunction with safety enhancement, we have been able to cut costs and increase productivity. There needs to be no compromise; the three are eminently compatible.'

Emergency response and evacuation plans were put into action as part of the onshore demonstration of safety management systems.

'Andrew's safety case is a live part of the platform operating system. It's a fundamental change from having a set of manuals sitting on the shelf'

Owen Chappell
Offshore installation manager BP

Quality with confidence

'There were initial concerns over the apparent contradiction of reducing costs while maintaining quality'

Paul Bibby
Project co-ordinator BP

For a North Sea development to announce that as part of its strategy to drive down costs it intended to pass direct responsibility for quality management from client to contractors, and at the same time end the tradition of continuous surveillance of suppliers, could have been interpreted as a recipe for producing a substandard offshore platform. But the final product tells a different story; for the quality of the Andrew facilities at least matches the high standards of other modern offshore installations.

'There were initial concerns over the apparent contradiction of reducing costs while maintaining quality,' admits Andrew project co-ordinator Paul Bibby. 'As client, we were handing responsibility for delivering quality products primarily to the alliance contractors, which is where it truly belongs. The interface between design and fabrication is a key element in this. Normally design deliverables are driven by deadlines, schedules and stage payments – incomplete or inaccurate documents can be issued purely to meet delivery dates and receive payment. But with the alignment of interests developed through the alliance, people recognised there was no benefit in producing substandard products. One alliance member or another would pick up on mistakes or shortcuts because everyone's profit depended on achieving a good result. The final outcome was a high standard of quality.'

From the early presanction phase, the project launched a three-pronged approach to quality management, addressing the performance of the alliance companies, equipment and materials suppliers, and the creation of a system which brought together the overall control of quality and its integration with health, safety and the environment.

'Full advantage was taken of Brown & Root's newly installed quality management system (QMS), certified to the internationally recognised ISO 9001 standard,' explains Andrew's quality manager Mike Blyton of Brown & Root. 'This was enhanced to provide the best value for Andrew's design and procurement phases, and also resulted in a simpler system than had previously been used.'

Early resolution of the controls that would be required for the management and co-ordination of interfaces on the project produced a set of procedures that were employed throughout the facilities development. Health, safety and environmental management systems were incorporated into Andrew's QMS. A comprehensive audit and review programme was compiled which encompassed quality, technical and safety audits, and those of the certifying authority Lloyd's Register, and the Health and Safety Executive. Through discussion, agreement was reached on the

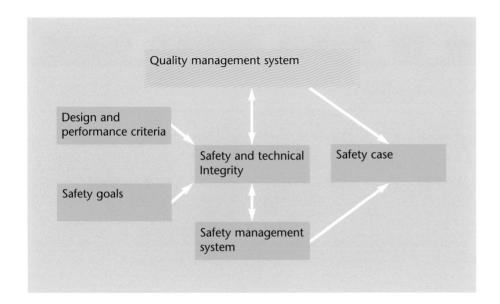

Andrew's quality management system incorporated safety management and generated procedures for the facilities development.

In the diagram: Quality management system; Design and performance criteria; Safety and technical Integrity; Safety case; Safety goals; Safety management system

scope of the audits, the exchange of information resulting in 'best value' and greater credibility for the audits within the project.

Alliance members – who had been selected through a process which had already established their commitment to quality and its improvement – were required to produce a quality plan for their individual activities and for the control of interfaces to one another. 'There was no interference with the management systems of the alliance members,' Blyton points out. 'These systems had been carefully assessed as a key part of contractor selection prior to contracts being let. During the project, quality control systems were reviewed and monitored to confirm they were in place. We were then able to publicise to the alliance with a high level of confidence that quality was being maintained.'

Supplier performance – the third main element in the quality plan – was identified as fundamental to Andrew's success. Time and effort were devoted to enrolling suppliers of equipment and materials into the project's goals, inviting companies to explain the problems they had experienced on past projects. Some clear messages were transmitted. Suppliers requested less client prescription and the opportunity to offer standard products; the volume of supplier documentation to be submitted for review should be reduced; and intervention by the project through expediting and inspection should be minimised. In return suppliers were prepared to accept responsibility for ensuring the quality of their products.

'We had learned from 'business as usual' that quality could not be built into equipment packages just by having an inspector in the factory,' acknowledges Blyton. 'Following that route would certainly run up manhours but would not necessarily guarantee a better product or delivery. For Andrew we chose to minimise our intervention and trust the suppliers to meet their promises.'

Quality with confidence

'We had learned from 'business as usual' that quality could not be built into equipment packages just by having an inspector in the factory'

Mike Blyton
Quality manager Brown & Root

As a basis for the transfer of responsibility, each supplier submitted a detailed quality plan to the project, identifying the mechanisms that would be used for self-regulation – the alternative to widespread field expediting and inspection effort being imposed by the Andrew team. The key was to establish mutual confidence in the plan, which would be subjected to quality assurance checks at agreed points in time by the project team – the usual 'hold' and 'witness' points were no longer stipulated. Over the course of the manufacturing period, lasting for eighteen months, some 300 assurance checks were made across Andrew's 130 principal package suppliers. By pursuing the minimum intervention approach, field expediting manhours on the project were eliminated, while inspection was more than halved.

The procurement process for equipment and materials – based upon the issue of simplified functional specifications rather than heavily prescriptive demands – was led by Andrew's package teams, bringing together engineering, quality, safety, operations and purchasing skills into five-man units, with responsibility for groups of purchase orders ranging in value from £300 to £9 million. For all packages, and most particularly the larger ones, establishing full understanding of their precise content was a critical step in the quality management process.

'The key to the effectiveness of the project's minimum intervention approach was to ensure the scope of supply was very clearly defined and agreed upon at the beginning of the contract through the bid optimisation process,' explains purchasing supervisor George Marsh. 'The bid optimisation process played an important part in securing best value for Andrew, analysing the prime bidder's tender in far more detail than the traditional bid clarification meetings. In some instances this produced a reduction in cost, but the lowest price was not the primary criterion for selection. Best value for Andrew was often achieved by spending more money, not less.'

Package team leader Tony Newton adds to this view. 'Developing more open relationships with suppliers was an essential element in the quality system. It used to be that the project set the ground rules, the supplier tried to meet them, then the project would point out where he'd gone wrong. It was an inefficient cycle involving two separate sides. On Andrew we set out together.'

A case in point which typified the close co-operation existing between the alliance and suppliers centres on the platform's three main power generation units, manufactured by European Gas Turbines (EGT). Package team and supplier's project team worked together to ensure both parties were aligned towards a common objective – that the duties stated in the project's non-prescriptive functional specification would be met by the standard machines offered by EGT, safely, on time and within budget – and that risks to achieving this goal were minimised. Steps in the manufacturing process which by tradition had frequently been included to satisfy burdensome client requirements were examined and rationalised, including dispensing with the conventional string test of coupled

'Best value for Andrew was often achieved by spending more money, not less'

George Marsh
Purchasing supervisor Brown & Root

Three main power generators installed at an early stage of outfitting on the weather deck.

turbines and generators, bringing substantial cost savings. On an order of this value – around £6 million – the project's quality team would by convention assign an engineer to be almost resident in the supplier's works, to sanction every decision and witness every action, thereby introducing delays into the manufacturing programme and adding costs for the project. But for Andrew's generators, continuous surveillance was not pursued. The confidence which grew from clarity of understanding and alignment of purpose between project and supplier meant that only occasional visits to the works were made by the package team – trust in EGT's project team to adhere to its quality plan without client intervention resulted in fully operational power generation packages delivered on time and within budget.

Andrew's QMS also called for less supplier documentation to be submitted to the project for review. 'A perception had grown up in the industry surrounding the extent of paperwork needed by client or certifying authority,' says David Cummergen, project manager for Lloyd's Register. 'The types and amount of documentation being submitted had grown well beyond useful levels. The fact that we were now working closely together, questioning normal practices, and listening to suppliers, enabled us to determine the true documentation needs of all parties. The reductions were drastic.'

Rather than request multiple copies of all drawings and documents generated during manufacturing for circulation throughout the project and certifying authority – welder qualifications, materials certificates and weight control procedures were typical of the many reports previously requested – these were held by the supplier, with only key documents being forwarded for review. In a similar way, the number of documents forwarded with packages to the construction sites

'With the allignment of interests developed through the alliance, people recognized there was no benefit in producing substandard products. Everyone's profit depended on achieving a good result'

Paul Bibby
Project co-ordinator BP

Quality with confidence

was also limited to essential items. For the operation of the Andrew field, the majority of documents held by the operations support group are stored in electronic form as part of the computerised Plant Manager system, with only a small percentage remaining as hard copies.

The quality and degree of completion of suppliers' packages arriving at the fabrication yards was perhaps the acid test for Andrew's 'hands off' approach to supplier performance. A review of the skills available within the alliance's design and fabrication contractors had led to the conclusion early in the project that the companies possessed most of the necessary expertise for installation and commissioning of equipment packages at the topsides construction site in Teesside. As a result, the project planned for a considerably lower level of supplier support at site than on previous projects, a step change which would largely depend on the success of Andrew's quality management strategy. But would that expectation be realised in practice? The evidence from Teesside speaks for itself. Around 90% of the packages either met the project's quality standards or were considered to show improvements compared with those received at the TJB yard on earlier projects; 98% of all purchase orders arrived at site before fabrication need dates; and no contractual claims arose between the project and suppliers – an outcome unheard of for a North Sea development of this size.

During design and fabrication of the platform's facilities, responsibility for quality lay principally with the alliance contractors – the main task for the quality management representatives was to ensure the agreed control systems were in place and were being correctly implemented. Continuous improvement of quality was strongly encouraged; the project's Opportunities for Improvement (OFI)

Decreased supplier support at site depended largely on the success of the project's quality management strategy.

programme was conceived and designed to provide both visibility in the drive for improvement, and to add a little competitive edge to the process.

'The OFI programme was instigated to stimulate the generation of new ideas and innovations across the Andrew and Cyrus alliances for all phases of the project,' relates programme co-ordinator Mike Blyton. 'It allows individuals and teams to contribute their visions for enhancing the way business is performed and results in an improved quality product, often with an associated reduction in cost. Although engineers naturally strive for improvement as part of their professional duty, the small awards made under the OFI scheme were all part of Andrew's teambuilding process.'

Under the programme, all suggestions without exception were given equal hearing, serving to remove the 'they never listen to me' attitude often encountered among members of large project teams. Suggestions came from individuals and groups, putting forward ideas for both technical and procedural improvements, over 300 in all. A fixed timetable for review and final evaluation by members of the alliance integrated management team was established, with all results – successes and failures – being published.

'Enhancement of the project's business performance was the principal yardstick for evaluating OFIs,' adds Blyton. 'While a measurable financial return was not a prerequisite, many ideas did result in economic benefits, some of them with major impact.' An example from one end of the OFI scale successfully suggested replacing stainless steel ventilation grilles in some platform areas with aluminium grilles, saving around £1000. At the other extreme, decreasing the number of jacket foundation piles from sixteen to twelve reduced overall costs to the alliance by over £3 million. OFIs which were successful sometimes attracted non-monetary awards – team social evenings and weekends away helped promote a degree of friendly competition within the project. The reward for Andrew and Cyrus stemming from the OFI programme was an estimated overall saving of £9 million.

Management of the wide range of licences, consents and permits required by the project was supported by a series of computer databases to help track the progress of regulatory compliance. In all, almost 700 activities were managed on the databases, achieving high levels of information dissemination to all interested parties.

'We set ourselves the challenge of bringing about a radical approach to the management of quality on Andrew,' reflects Mike Blyton. 'It was recognised to be a high risk strategy that we were introducing and much would depend on the attitude and commitment of the whole project team, contractors and suppliers. Time spent in building relationships resulted in understanding one another's problems and helped to resolve issues by co-operation. We believe the project's approach has delivered the required quality in the main. However, the true test will come during platform operations over the first years of field life.'

'The OFI programme allows individuals and teams to contribute their visions for enhancing business performance'

Mike Blyton
Quality manager Brown & Root

Behaviour: Sparking the fire

'It is the creation of this atmosphere which has been the major change on Andrew, the shift to the single identity of a unified team'

John Martin
Project manager BP

From the time Andrew made its reappearance for development at the forefront of BP's drive for cost reduction, there was no doubt in the minds of the project team that a level of performance over and above that of previous North Sea projects would be demanded if the field was to be converted into a valued asset. As the team explored and later crystallised its vision for Andrew, two vital ingredients were identified to be essential in the equation for realising the project's ambitious development plan. Those ingredients were technology and behaviour.

Innovative engineering solutions were encouraged and adopted throughout the project. Andrew's streamlined jacket and pile design, electronic interchange of information between designers and fabricators, and the application of advanced construction techniques were prominent among them. On the seabed, new pipeline and bundle technologies pushed up the efficiency of operations, while onshore, detailed planning across alliance contractors and suppliers delivered the completion of the integrated deck, itself installed in a dynamically positioned lift operation rated as the world's heaviest to date.

The project's array of innovative technical solutions played its part in Andrew's successful reduction of capital development cost. But many of these advances may not have been pursued were it not for the climate of challenge and co-operation

Adversity, contractual conflict and a 'who's to blame' culture – the hallmarks of traditional working – were pronounced unwelcome by the Andrew team.

which surrounded the Andrew development, one which BP project manager John Martin ascribes to a fundamental change in the behaviour of individuals.

'From the experience of past attempts to develop Andrew, we were keenly aware that technology alone would not provide the economic performance required,' he comments. 'Technology needed a partner. We believed the ingredient which had been missing was the correct behaviour, the attitude which governs the relationships between companies and individuals, which enables ideas to come forward in an open fashion, and which bonds people to pull together when problems arise. It is the creation of this atmosphere which has been the major change on Andrew, the shift to the single identity of a unified team.'

The belief that technology and behaviour were the twin building blocks vital to Andrew's success was evident from the outset. In forming the alliance, the process of contractor selection was designed to ascertain as much about attitudes and receptiveness to co-operation as it was to determining technical competence. BP's 'Minimum Conditions of Satisfaction', along with the opportunities for contractors to stipulate their expectations of the client and to influence the selection of successive members of the alliance, combined to set the tone of the project. Adversity, contractual conflict and a 'who's to blame' culture – the hallmarks of traditional working – were pronounced unwelcome. A single team, aligned to a common business goal, was advocated as the alternative which could deliver a satisfactory result.

Such an alternative may have appeared to be a worthy ideal, but in reality demanded a step change in attitude and habits which had built up over decades of 'business as usual'. Companies and individuals had become used to taking partisan stances over issues and problems, a response which would not be automatically dislodged simply by stating the alliance was a single team – action was also required.

'We had made a good start with the careful selection of the contractors and individuals within the team,' states Martin. 'This had given us impetus but now we needed to maintain that, to actively sustain a teambuilding environment. We had already begun to sense the 'Spirit of Andrew' during presanction – now we had to allow that to flourish.'

The 'top down' commitment which cascaded through the project set out to enroll all participants in Andrew's vision and goals. Individuals were empowered to make decisions – the absence of man-for-man marking placed new demands and responsibilities on Andrew's team members, who had no recourse to a conventional shadow client team. The drive was to create a 'total team' where everyone was valued equally, dispelling the 'them and us' viewpoint.

'When we began we saw one another as representatives of companies, and held opinions based on company reputations,' recalls Bill Ebdon of Brown & Root.

Behaviour: Sparking the fire

'Company identity became almost irrelevant to us and largely indistinguishable to the outside observer'

Bill Ebdon
Brown & Root

'But as we became clear on what we were trying to achieve together, those preconceptions faded and people were treated according to individual character. We were clearing away the old baggage. Company identity became almost irrelevant to us and largely indistinguishable to the outside observer.'

New members joining the team underwent a comprehensive induction presentation, explaining Andrew's goals, financial targets and the open nature of communication on the project. Individuals were given the freedom to challenge accepted practice, to seek ways to eradicate costs which did not add value. The clear statement that everyone in the team had the potential and the right to contribute was a powerful recognition which helped people shed the restrictions of the past and come forward with constructive suggestions without fear of encountering adverse reaction; equally important was the expectation that such suggestions would be addressed rather than ignored. Traditional client-contractor hierarchies were eliminated by the formation of the integrated management team. 'Once we realised that the historic tiers of authority, cross checking and approval were gone – that we were no longer waiting for permission – we grasped the freedom with relish,' adds Ebdon.

While such measures were proving effective in breaking down barriers and permitting an atmosphere of unity and co-operation to grow, the team recognised it did not have all the answers for arriving at its stated goals, for pushing itself to increasingly higher performance levels. External coaching and guidance were also necessary to assist the team to explore its potential, and to help individuals maintain the stamina demanded for continuously setting new targets.

Behind the daily activities of the project a programme of education was ongoing to achieve just that. Management consulting firm JMW Consultants, experienced in assisting corporations to achieve performance breakthroughs, had been engaged since the time of project presanction to support the Andrew team in its commitment to achieving an extraordinary result. JMW had already established connections with BP, both at a corporate level and through the Hyde offshore development project, where the company's support had contributed to a successful outcome. Key members of the Andrew project team, around fifty in total, attended intensive JMW management courses designed to elevate performance levels and expand leadership ability in a changing business climate.

'The courses helped us understand what a team could really do and identified the barriers which stood in the way of achieving outstanding results,' observes John Jerzak of BP. 'We gained a fresh perspective on leadership and learned to live with the discomfort which comes from continuously extending your targets. Above all we learned that the only true way to influence the project was to be a player, not a spectator. This gave us the confidence to take ownership of problems and commit to sorting them out.'

Many people perceived the courses to be expounding 'well packaged common sense' rather than profound revelations. But the key lay in JMW's translation of that common sense into useful practical tools that could be applied to the running of a demanding project to obtain the desired results.

'I had doubts about the value of the JMW courses initially,' says Saipem's alliance board member Jim Grice. 'But in time I became convinced it was money well spent. The courses made people think about the things accepted as norms. This was clearly displayed in target setting, but it went much deeper than that. Individuals were continuously challenging themselves; it helped bring out the best in the team.'

Teambuilding indisputably benefited from the coaching programme, but the underlying purpose was more keenly focused, as deputy project manager Ash Bakshi of Brown & Root points out. 'Everything we were learning was tied to a business result. We were being taught to set challenges, state what we stood for, and commit to achieving exceptional targets – the more you stretch yourself, the better you perform. But we were not dealing with soft issues. We were chasing a serious financial goal with the opportunity to increase significantly our normal level of profits.'

Behaviour: Sparking the fire

'Individuals were
continuously
challenging themselves;
it helped bring out the
best in the team'

Jim Grice
Alliance board member Saipem

Setting and achieving stretched targets became a primary mechanism in Andrew's
ultimate success, one which can be directly linked to the JMW influence.
In addition to the management courses, the company also organised 'away days'
for the team, workshop sessions removed from the project's design and fabrication
locations which enabled individuals and groups to unearth their concerns and
pinpoint key issues which needed resolution. The sessions were designed to
reinvigorate the team, continuing the process of enrolment in group decisions, and
are acknowledged to have helped align the energies of the team – 'clearing away
our deficiencies to get to the important issues,' as John Martin puts it.

But the clearest demonstration of the successful partnership between JMW
and the Andrew alliance lies in the successive stretched targets which were set
during the away day sessions. At a workshop immediately following project
sanction in February 1994, the team had set a major challenge by committing to a
target cost of £320 million, slicing over £50 million from the figure sanctioned only
one week earlier. Another session saw the advent of Andrew's ambitious 110%
onshore completion concept and the exclusion of the traditional flotel during
hookup. A further occasion gave rise to the team's final target cost for the project
of £290 million. All stretched targets, though appearing to be out of reach at the
time, were met.

'It was not easy for us to commit to such ambitious targets at first,' notes
Ebdon. 'As engineers we didn't see how we could achieve them and the risks
were all too prevalent. The difference came when JMW freed us from the fear

of failure – we were not being asked to give a guarantee, this was another sort of promise; if we didn't meet the target we would not be viewed as failures. But the risks remained and whenever it looked as though we might reach the target, we set a more challenging one. This created a sense of imbalance which kept us moving ahead.'

John Martin recognises that the part played by external coaching made a dramatic difference to the project's outcome. 'The key difference was the setting of stretched targets for Andrew – without these we would not have achieved so much. But the entire project has undoubtedly fired people's enthusiasm; the fuel for that fire is the people, the oxygen is the freedom we have been granted, and the spark that ignited it came from JMW.'

The fire of enthusiasm he refers to tapped hidden energy resources within the team which spilled over from professional duties to be channelled into a variety of activities under the project's ethos of 'work smart but have fun'. Funds were raised for charity through long distance races, the operations team cycled from London to Teesside and a year later – while the integrated deck was en route for the field – sixty people travelled to Gambia where the team set to work erecting and completing a village primary school. Social functions were a regular feature of the project, on one occasion even including a musical written and staged by team members. The Andrew logo, nicknamed the 'Hot Cross Onion', became synonymous with the project's lighthearted and popular newsletter.

Thus, the 'Spirit of Andrew' represented more than the unstinting efforts of the alliance in heading towards a common business goal; a true team was built and motivated, worked hard, had fun, and delivered an exceptional result. Saipem's Jim Grice, acknowledged to be one of the industry's most experienced figures, summarises the effect. 'Of all the contracts I've worked on around the world, Andrew is the most successful measured in terms of the satisfaction gained by those involved.'

'The key difference was the setting of stretched targets for Andrew – without these we would not have achieved so much'

John Martin
Project manager BP

Andrew delivers

'To install a North Sea platform and produce oil six weeks later is a tribute to the Andrew team. Three years ago we would not have believed this was possible'

John Martin
Project manager BP

Seven days in May

On 12 May 1996, Andrew's integrated deck appeared over the North Sea horizon following its two day voyage to the field from the Moray Firth. The asset development team was now facing its sternest test. Would first oil be flowing only six weeks later, as the team had planned, or would the notorious difficulties of offshore completion force a lapse into traditional working and delay production?

Jacket and piles installation had been completed; now Saipem's *S7000* semisubmersible crane vessel was preparing for the lift of the integrated deck. With the jacket pile grouting operation tested and accepted by Lloyd's Register, in the afternoon of 13 May Andrew's deck was raised from the *Giant 4* transportation barge by the huge twin cranes of *S7000*. With the 10,274t load suspended high above the waves, the vessel moved across to the waiting jacket.

'The entire operation was carried out using the vessel's dynamic positioning (DP) system,' reports Saipem's alliance project manager Tony Press. 'This sets a new world record for a DP lift, and in addition is the largest single structure ever lifted onto a BP installation. Using DP instead of the vessel's anchor spread saved time and avoided having to work around the subsea facilities and pipelines already in place.'

In the space of three hours the massive structure had been carefully landed onto the jacket; two days later, the 138t flare tower, which had been transported by separate barge to the field, was lifted into place. Andrew's platform facilities were now united, well within the scheduled installation window despite the holdups caused by inclement North Sea weather.

The project was now entering what was perhaps its most rigorously planned – and pressured – phase of activity. 'The alliance had been working toward this point for almost two years,' observes BP completions manager Roy Timms. 'We had built our plan on completing the offshore phase without a specialist hookup contractor or supporting flotel, and through the 110% onshore completion strategy had done everything to minimise the tasks remaining. The next key steps were to obtain approval for inhabiting the platform and beginning the tie-back of wells. We had set ourselves a target of achieving this in just seven days.'

As a result of the innovative onshore completions programme, Andrew's integrated deck had been granted a 'draft Certificate of Fitness' by Lloyd's Register while still at Teesside, a move unprecedented in the industry. Though the full and final certificate could not be issued until the platform was installed and completed in the field, the draft certificate stipulated certain actions to be fulfilled offshore, necessary to lift limitations and endow the platform with approval for habitation,

Supporting over 10,000t from its twin cranes, *S7000* carries the integrated deck towards the waiting jacket.

drilling and finally production. Central to the plan was the employment of the *S7000* as support vessel, only the second occasion that the sophisticated crane barge would be used for an offshore hookup contract.

'The industry's usual procedure for offshore hookup is to engage a flotel to sit alongside the platform to support a large workforce possibly a thousand strong, with durations running into months,' Timms points out. 'This is where offshore costs have historically grown very significantly as the workforce discovers all the surprises which arise due to incomplete onshore construction and commissioning. Had the alliance followed that route, the likelihood is that the £24 million allocated for offshore hookup and commissioning in the sanction budget   a figure which had escalated to £27 million over the intervening period – would have been swallowed up, and a large portion of the unallocated provision would have disappeared too.'

Instead the alliance had opted for the *S7000* in an ambitious offshore strategy which, despite the higher daily cost of the specialised vessel, promised to bring savings of £20 million to the project. But the plan brought its own pressures.

Seven days in May

Moment of mating for the deck
and jacket.

The duration for *S7000's* supporting role was scheduled to be only seven days.
In this remarkably short time the alliance was committing to achieving both
platform habitation within two days and readiness for drilling five days later.
The offshore minimisation programme had been highly effective in its challenge
to accepted practices by designing out offshore work from an early stage, and
identifying all tasks which could be completed at Teesside rather than carrying
them offshore. As a result, the programme to achieve Certificate of Fitness for
Drilling in seven days contained a direct work content of only 7500 offshore
manhours. At this level, Andrew would be breaking all records for offshore
completion by more than an order of magnitude.

North Sea platforms in the early 1980s had consumed manhours for offshore
completion at rates of up to 150 manhours per tonne of installed topsides – BP's
Magnus platform required over 4.5 million manhours to complete the 30,000t
modularised topsides. Ten years later, topsides had generally become smaller and
lighter, while the advent of the giant crane vessel permitted single lift integrated
decks with the advantage of more advanced onshore commissioning levels.
Offshore completion manhours reflected this trend by a corresponding reduction,
but still clustered around the 30-70 manhours per tonne range. In 1994, the 9100t

integrated deck for Total's Dunbar platform achieved a record-setting 20 manhours per tonne. But now, in 1996, Andrew had set its sights on a seemingly impossible 45 minutes per tonne.

In the wake of the successful 110% onshore completion strategy, the concentrated offshore work phase was also prominently designated to ensure it remained a focus of attention with a high profile. 'Seven days in May' neatly encapsulated the campaign-like nature of the challenging offshore exercise. To undertake that campaign, the alliance had formed an integrated taskforce built from Saipem's project members and vessel crew, the platform operations team, Santa Fe's drilling team, TJB's workforce, Brown & Root engineering support, and specialist subcontractors. As alliance diving contractor for Andrew and Cyrus, Rockwater would also begin completion of the pipeline connections to the platform. The 300-strong force would undertake the seven-day programme to prepare the platform for drilling, at which point *S7000* would sail from the Andrew field.

'The intensity of the work programme and allocation of tasks to individuals and groups called for precise planning at a detailed level,' explains BP completions engineer Brian Gebruers. 'For this, the scope of work had to be understood and controlled very accurately for which we used a computerised database of job cards, imparting clear visibility to the tasks to be performed – when, by whom, and for how long. It was a practical tool which gave us the insight and confidence we needed that the seven day programme was achievable, and, very importantly, who had ownership of each specific offshore job.'

The job card database, developed by the project team in conjunction with BP's information technology group at Sunbury, allocated tasks and their durations at a detailed level, down to one or two hours in some cases. In all, some 400 jobs were logged, taking account of the limits placed upon the number of personnel which could be present on the platform under the limitations of the 'draft Certificate of Fitness'. Fifty people were permitted to be onboard until initial life support systems were established, followed by up to 100 prior to habitation approval. After this, a total of 144 were allowed to work on the platform, reducing to the normal maximum complement of 72 when *S7000* departed. Unlike conventional job card systems, the database permitted sorting of jobs by platform area, process system, completion status, programmed start date and Certificate of Fitness. Combined with this, each job card had attached to it a workpack of instructions, supporting drawings, and permits-to-work – written and risk assessed onshore, awaiting signature offshore. In theory there was effectively no opportunity for the offshore programme to expand. 'We were determined to capture the offshore growth phantom,' asserts Timms.

Lights on as night falls on the day of deck installation.

'We were determined to capture the offshore growth phantom'

Roy Timms
Completions manager BP

Seven days in May

But in the offshore world, even the best laid plans are subject to unexpected change. Hard on the heels of Andrew's successful platform installation, the North Sea weather again took a turn for the worse. It appeared that as Andrew was heading for the finishing line, some of the good fortune associated with the project might be about to run out.

Access between *S7000* and the platform was via a bridge gangway, a steel structure which could be raised or lowered, depending on the sea state and relative motion between the floating vessel and fixed platform. Poor weather beginning on 14 May and lasting for three days restricted the availability of the bridge connection. The situation did not improve until the middle of 17 May, delaying the start of the seven day programme, and even then, 'permanent' bridge access remained very limited.

'Over the course of the week, the bridge was out of action for around 80% of the time,' says alliance planning supervisor Clive Spackman of Brown & Root. 'This had a significant impact on the plan either by preventing certain teams reaching the platform, or detaining others onboard. The unexpected change in access coupled with the known manning level constraints created a major challenge to achieve the tight programme set for the seven days.'

Faced with the additional access constraint, the offshore team found a worthy ally in the computerised job card system. The circumstances could have caused considerable confusion, requiring the correct mix of skills to be present on the platform during each upcoming shift, at the same time keeping within specified manning levels. But the visibility provided by the system directly aided decision making on a shift-by-shift basis, enabling flexible planning of the next shift's work and tracking of progress. The high level of preparatory work which had been carried out onshore paid off in full, as individuals were fully familiar with the procedures for each task and were not unduly thrown off course by the unexpected disruptions encountered. Within a few hours of the seven day programme getting into its proper stride, initial safety systems were all recommissioned and certified; main power generators were operating within twelve hours; the galley in the

Offshore completion scope	Remove installation aids
Topsides completion	Drilling facility completion
Pull and connect hazardous drains caisson	**Subsea riser tie-ins**
Connect flare tower lines	Tie-in Cyrus 10" line
Remove seafastenings	Tie-in oil export line
Tie-in oil and gas export lines	Tie-in gas export line
Temporary supply connections	Commission and test export lines
Install seawater and firewater pumps	**Platform tie-backs**
Remove spreader bar column and braces	Flowline connections to four template wells

accommodation unit was feeding one hundred people after only 24 hours. Certificate of Fitness for Habitation was granted by Lloyd's Register 12 hours later, with firewater systems and helideck in operation. The platform could now be inhabited around the clock. The operations team, which had lived in the accommodation module for three months at Teesside, reported they were 'pleased to have returned home'.

Although high winds and sea states continued to hamper some activities – welding work on the flare and underdeck pipework in particular – the taskforce pushed on towards its seven day goal. As each assignment reached completion, acceptance was given by the certifying authority; one by one the limitations listed in the onshore 'draft Certificate of Fitness' were lifted. On 22 May the team could see the target was within reach and informed *S7000* that the final shift would end at noon on the following day. To mark the event Saipem superintendent Erchole Baldoni, in charge of the crane vessel, crossed the bridge to enjoy dinner as the

Seven days in May

'The seven days were remarkable, not only for the intensity of the work carried out, but also for the fact that the period was entirely free from accidents'

Owen Chappell
Offshore installation manager BP

guest of the platform's operations team, a gesture of hospitality made possible by the unique accomplishment of Andrew's accelerated offshore completion. At midday on 24 May, the platform received its Certificate of Fitness for Drilling – 'Seven days in May' had fulfilled both its name and purpose.

In terms of manhours expended, no significant growth was experienced during the period. All job carded tasks for the planned 7500 direct manhours were completed, plus the 300 manhours carried over from onshore completion at Hartlepool. Other time was spent in supervisory roles, and by the certifying authority; the drilling crew, which remained on the platform full time after habitation was approved, brought forward some of the predrilled well tie-back tasks into the seven day period. Precise quantification of the total number of work hours was made slightly difficult by people having to remain on the platform, trapped by weather; others were able to move to and fro by helicopter shuttle. A detailed estimate accounting for all these factors puts the number of effective hours at 10,476. Based on this figure, hookup of Andrew's integrated deck was achieved at a level of one manhour per tonne of installed topsides.

'Despite the difficulties imposed by weather and the resulting access restrictions, we had realised our first major milestone of offshore completion as planned,' says BP offshore installation manager Owen Chappell. 'The seven days were remarkable, not only for the intensity of the work carried out by the alliance, but also for the fact that the period was entirely free from accidents. We have always accorded safety top priority in our mission to complete onshore and minimise offshore work; the accident-free record for offshore completion underscores the clear safety benefits of the strategy.'

With *S7000* now departed from the field, the final stages of preparation for first oil began. Rockwater's diving support vessel *Semi 2* moved into the field to complete the connections from the platform to the export pipelines and to Cyrus, by installing pipeline spools on the seabed near the base of the jacket. Pipeline commissioning followed – all went well for the oil export line, but a stuck 'pig' in the gas line caused a few headaches before it was finally freed. As part of Andrew's well engineering alliance, Santa Fe continued work on tying back the field's four predrilled wells, while the platform operations team concentrated on flowline hookup and preparations for startup. Problems were encountered and resolved, including mechanical trouble with one firewater pump and realignment of the gas reinjection compressor train. But the advanced degree of preparedness secured during the onshore completion programme paid dividends, supporting the transition to hydrocarbon service.

On 12 June, the Health & Safety Executive approved the platform's operations safety case; six days later Lloyd's Register issued the full Certificate of Fitness for

Diving support vessel *Semi 2* alongside the platform to complete subsea tie-ins.

Production. At 18.00 hours on 26 June oil began flowing from Andrew's first well at an initial rate of 3500 barrels per day. The ever tightening targets for first oil which the Andrew facilities team had imposed on itself and lived with for over two years had been met – and in style. Compared to original expectations, oil was now flowing over six months early.

'To install a North Sea platform and produce oil six weeks later is a tribute to the Andrew team,' states BP project manager John Martin. 'Three years ago we would not have believed this was possible.'

An extraordinary result

In the weeks that followed first oil, Andrew's three remaining predrilled wells were quickly completed by the operations alliance, one of them in a period of only twelve days, enabling production levels to rise rapidly towards the field's 58,000bpd plateau. In July 1996, a month after the platform had come on stream, the Cyrus subsea development followed suit, adding further production to the oil export pipeline which by early August was transporting over 70,000bpd from the two fields to shore. Gas began to flow from the Andrew field soon afterwards, bound for customer Scottish Power.

The result of the Andrew alliance venture was now there for all to see. A development challenge which three years earlier had been tagged 'a dog of a project' had been transformed from a weak prospect in BP's North Sea portfolio to a valued producing asset. A field which for more than twenty years had stubbornly refused to yield its reserves economically, had finally been brought into productive life as a commercial triumph – exceptionally below budget and over six months ahead of schedule.

When the Andrew journey began, it had stood for change on many fronts. For BP, a new level of business performance was sought, one which would breathe fresh life into the North Sea in an ever more competitive era. For the wider industry, it presented an opportunity to test the potential of a fully-fledged alliance of contractors, aligned to a common financial goal and ready to dispel the adversarial behaviour of the past. For individuals, Andrew held out the chance to free themselves from the constraints of historical working methods, to unlock inner abilities and challenge traditional practice. With the field now in operation, those intentions can be assessed against the outcome.

Andrew drilling crew at work.

Economic evaluation of the project leaves no room for doubt in acknowledging its success. Even until four years ago, the estimated cost to develop Andrew's facilities remained prohibitive at £450 million. With the formation of the facilities alliance between BP and seven main contractors and the commitment to move away from 'business as usual', that cost was driven down to £373 million by the end of 1993, enabling the project to receive sanction from BP and its licence partners. But at this level the project was given only a 38% probability of achieving its target cost. Step by step the unpredicted power of the alliance not only discovered the means to reach the target, it regularly revised its forecast, stretching first towards £320 million, then £290 million. The final cost for

Flare lit as first oil flows in June 1996.

delivering Andrew's platform and subsea facilities rested just below £290 million.

'When we received sanction two and a half years ago, I would never have thought such a reduction was achievable,' emphasises BP project manager John Martin. 'If we had come on stream a month early or saved £20 million, I would have considered that fantastic. But to achieve this degree of cost reduction and produce oil six months ahead of schedule was never in my wildest dreams at that time. It exceeds all possible expectations.'

Judged against the same parameters applied during the presanction risk assessment of Andrew, the platform would have been given less than 10% chance of being completed within the outturn cost of £290 million. Compared with the best estimate of £450 million for building Andrew's facilities at the time when BP called for a 30% reduction in offshore capital development costs across its assets, the project has beaten the company's target; compared with the reality of the far more challenging sanction estimate, the result represents a 23% decrease in planned expenditure. The fall in the project's capital cost has contributed significantly to Andrew's attractiveness as an economic investment for the development partners, with the project also standing as a positive milestone in the refocussing of business performance within BP.

BP group chief executive John Browne, who remembers Andrew's obstinate reputation from first hand experience as a young engineer in the company, puts the achievement in perspective.

'When around 1990 we reassessed how best to use our capital, the first challenge we decided to take on was the apparently impossible one – how do we develop Andrew? It was undertaken as the first breakthrough challenge by the

'To achieve this degree of cost reduction and produce oil six months ahead of schedule was never in my wildest dreams at that time'

John Martin
Project manager BP

An extraordinary result

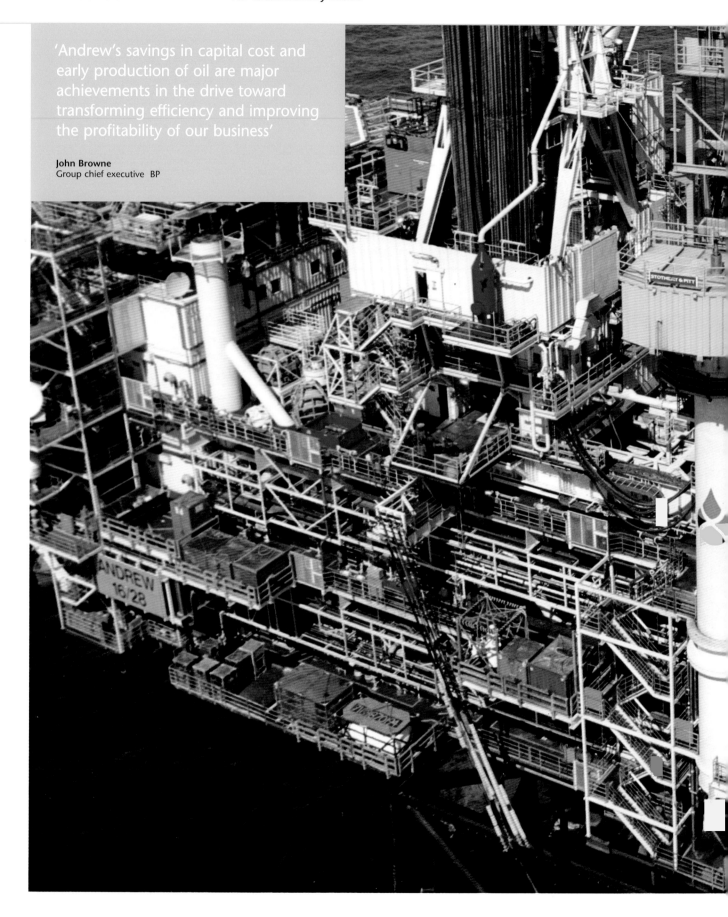

'Andrew's savings in capital cost and early production of oil are major achievements in the drive toward transforming efficiency and improving the profitability of our business'

John Browne
Group chief executive BP

An extraordinary result

asset team; it didn't work at the first attempt, but time and effort have proved it could be done. Bringing together subsurface and engineering skills in a fully integrated approach has made the project an outstanding success, and relationships have been built to the mutual advantage of everyone involved. The savings in capital cost and early production of oil are major achievements in the drive toward transforming efficiency and improving the profitability of our business.'

For BP's licence partners in the development – LASMO, Mitsubishi Oil, Clyde Petroleum and Talisman Energy – Andrew's performance has also imparted economic rewards beyond those originally hoped for, as observed by Roy Franklin, who once worked as a geologist on the Andrew discovery well and is now group managing director of Clyde Petroleum.

'At the time when Clyde bought its stake in Andrew in 1994 it was on the basis that material value would be added through project cost reductions, an acceleration in the development timetable, and better than anticipated reservoir performance,' he recounts. 'Little did I suspect that the Andrew facilities team would deliver on the first two in such spectacular fashion. It is an excellent example for the industry of what can be achieved by well-structured alliancing.'

Indeed the alliance is identified as the primary driving force at the forefront of Andrew's success. The vision for Andrew recognised that management of contractual interfaces had been a constant source of inefficiency for the industry, frequently giving rise to cost growth and delays in project schedules. While some form of close collaboration between client and contractors had been accepted as a vital ingredient if Andrew was to proceed, the exact form of that relationship and its management was unknown at the outset.

'We were aware that a step change was needed to bring about the jump in performance levels we were seeking,' affirms project co-ordinator Paul Bibby. 'The contractor selection process was fundamental to this; establishing the alliance prior to sanction ensured all major value decisions were made early. Rather than the traditional way of doing business where the client sets the price and the contractors try to meet it, for Andrew we enrolled companies and individuals into a team which created its own targets. The commitment to achieving those targets grew from that ownership.'

Acting as a single team became the focus of the project's identity, aligning the alliance members toward a common business objective with mutually shared interests. BP's presence in the team was kept to a minimum with no man-for-man marking, while contracts were designed to eliminate the adversarial conflicts of the finger-pointing 'blame culture' which had previously characterised many North Sea projects. 'We were not consumed by the past; we stuck together through thick and thin,' remarks John Martin.

'Little did I suspect that the Andrew facilities team would deliver on cost reduction and early oil in such spectacular fashion'

Roy Franklin
Group managing director
Clyde Petroleum

Commercial manager Barry Smale comments on the alliance contracts. 'Handling the contractual and legal sides of the project has been very straightforward – you might almost say simple by comparison with conventional jobs. The usual problems of closing out contracts involving extended negotiations, claims and counterclaims have not occurred – major alliance contracts were closed out the day after first oil, earlier in some cases. All alliance contracts came in under budget, and there have been no contractual claims to deal with.'

Corporate interests in the project were reinforced by the gainshare agreement, providing an opportunity to enhance company profits. As a yardstick for measuring the economic performance of Andrew for both licence partners and alliance members, the gainshare is emphatic in its result. By reducing costs far below the sanctioned budget, the contracting alliance was able to save for BP and its partners almost £40 million from the money sanctioned to be spent. Contractors found themselves in the unusual but highly rewarding position of sharing some £45 million, earned over and above normal contractual profits and directly attributable to the focusing of minds and energies encouraged by the alliance environment.

Alongside the impressive financial savings, Andrew's early production of oil brought revenues from the field forward by more than six months. Although the platform installation date remained fixed from the project's outset, the elimination of a lengthy offshore hookup and commissioning period accelerated the programme to first oil. Innovative thinking, close teamworking – combined with a skill in setting unlikely targets yet always meeting them – armed the alliance with the ability to accomplish its new offshore completion record, vastly improving overall working safety and saving £20 million into the bargain.

'In thirty years in the oil industry, and twenty within BP, I have no experience of a project not touching a penny of its contingency money, nor coming in six months early,' declares John Martin. 'Furthermore, I've never heard of a project where the operations crew lived in the accommodation module onshore for three months, nor a project which saved £20 million out of its offshore hookup budget and completed the hookup within a week.'

Delivering against targets became an established trademark of Andrew's team behaviour. Before the project began, BP had acknowledged that to improve business ventures beyond the benefits gained from technological advances alone, the necessary partner for technology lay in the cultivation of a positive behavioural attitude. This was sought and identified from the outset through the responses of the alliance contractors during selection, and was encouraged throughout the project at an individual level with continuous coaching of leadership skills and the active promotion of teambuilding.

An extraordinary result

A view commonly held by all participants in Andrew is that behaviour made the key difference to the project's outcome. 'If we had made any sort of savings, no matter how modest, we could have claimed the project was a success,' says Paul Bibby. 'Although the economic result is satisfying, the significant change here is the teamwork. The commitment to function as a single unit started at the top and cascaded to everyone. The gainshare alone would not have achieved the same results.'

Talk to anyone who worked on Andrew and they will report the sense of being 'freed', how they were invited to challenge existing practice, how they were given responsibility to make decisions. In this climate of co-operation, innovation and commitment came forward in abundance. 'We all learned a lot about the art of dealing with people,' observes John Martin. 'The atmosphere created on Andrew released the team to set its own targets and motivated people to deliver. Problems arose as they do on any project of this size, but it was the form of response that made the difference – the rate of overcoming difficulties was stunning.'

The effectiveness of the alliance way of working also proved valuable for the Cyrus project, which like Andrew, came in over 20% under sanction budget. As the influence of the facilities alliances grew, additional contracting groups were formed to execute other stages of Andrew's development. The field's well engineering alliance, the first of its kind in the offshore industry, was created between BP and four companies – Baker Hughes Inteq, Santa Fe, Schlumberger and Transocean – in September 1995 to complete Andrew's template wells; with the exception of Santa Fe, the same group carried out drilling of the two Cyrus subsea wells. Drilling and completion was successful on all five wells, with one Andrew horizontal well setting an industry record for rate of progress, while for Cyrus new standards of efficiency were achieved for subsea completion and production tree

'Although the economic result is satisfying, the significant change here is the teamwork. The gainshare alone would not have achieved the same results'

Paul Bibby
Project co-ordinator BP

installation. Andrew's seven-member operations alliance, finalised in July 1996, will support platform operations including drilling throughout the life of the field, assisted by suballiances of equipment suppliers and specialist services.

'The Andrew facilities alliance undoubtedly improved the project economics for BP and its partners,' states Robert Brown, who assumed the role of Andrew and Cyrus asset manager in 1996. 'The partners remained supportive of the approach throughout the development, helping to furnish the alliance with the space to innovate. Now we have an innovative operations alliance, which we are optimistic will deliver further benefits to all parties through close alignment. The facilities team has demonstrated very clearly that you can set targets and exceed your expectations – now we must ensure the success of the facilities and well engineering alliances is carried forward during operations.'

'The facilities team has demonstrated very clearly that you can set targets and exceed your expectations – now we must ensure the success of the facilities and well engineering alliances is carried forward during operations'

Robert Brown
Andrew and Cyrus asset manager BP

The Andrew team is united in the view that its methods are by no means a blueprint for success, nor indeed the only alliance model which could work. But within BP's wider activities, other projects have taken a keen interest in the achievements of Andrew and are now taking the alliance principles forward to build their own success. In the North Sea, the Eastern Trough Area Project (ETAP), a complex of seven oil and gas accumulations under development at a cost of £1.3 billion, is being conducted under an alliance agreement between operator BP, its coventurers and a group of contractors. Other alliances have been formed to execute the pioneering Foinaven and Schiehallion developments west of Shetland. The principles of alliancing are also embodied in the Badami onshore oilfield development in Alaska, the expansion of a polyethylene plant being constructed by BP Chemicals and its partners in Indonesia, and again in the refurbishment of BP's Grangemouth refinery in Scotland.

Interest in Andrew is not confined only to developments which involve BP. Over the course of the project, members of the team were invited to share their knowledge and experience with a wide range of companies and organisations, both within and outside the oil industry. Some forty presentations were given in countries as far afield as Australia and Colombia, addressing representatives from oil companies and project developments, contractors, civil engineering and automotive industries, government departments and academic institutions. In 1995 in the United Kingdom, BP received the new Department of Trade and Industry 'Innovation in Industry' award for its Andrew alliance contracting strategy.

The influence of the project is also being spread by the alliance contractors and wide spectrum of suppliers which enjoyed successful participation in delivering Andrew's facilities, and which are now finding new doors opening to them. Among these, Brown & Root's contribution to the project and subsequent reward is noted by Dick Cheney, chief executive of parent company Halliburton Energy Services. 'The success of Brown & Root's involvement in the Andrew alliance

An extraordinary result

has helped to open discussions on a wide range of other alliances and integrated services contracts, some of which will come to fruition in 1996,' he confirms.

Project manager John Martin looks back at the Andrew project as an achievement the entire team can be proud of, having moved away from 'business as usual' in the offshore industry to accomplish what was once viewed as the impossible challenge of transforming Andrew into a commercial success.

'In delivering the Andrew facilities we have set new benchmarks for cost saving and the level of onshore completion. We have turned possibilities into realities and shown what can be achieved when working in the non-adversarial spirit of an alliance. But let's be clear, while we have strived hard and made great progress, the challenges still remain; there is a long way to go.

'Our success with the Andrew project is now for others to judge. It is only the start of realising the value of the Andrew asset, and long term success remains to be achieved over the life of the field. However, from the perspective of the alliance, Andrew will always stand as an extraordinary result.'

Andrew platform facilities in production six months early in June 1996.

Andrew and Cyrus
fields schematic

Andrew and Cyrus fields
facts and figures

Development partners
and alliance members

Facilities development schedule

Facilities subcontractors
and suppliers

About the author

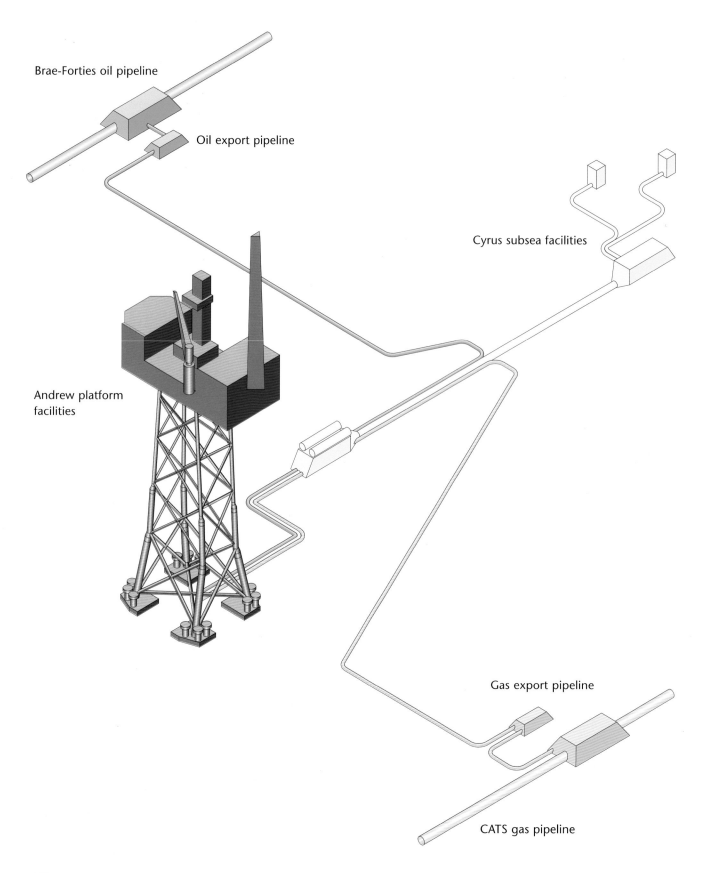

Brae-Forties oil pipeline

Oil export pipeline

Cyrus subsea facilities

Andrew platform
facilities

Gas export pipeline

CATS gas pipeline

Andrew field

Location UK Blocks 16/27a and 16/28 230km north east of Aberdeen

Discovery June 1974

Water depth 115m

Reservoir Palaeocene sandstone oil accumulation with associated gas cap, lying approximately

2500m below seabed; 58m thick oil column

Recoverable reserves Estimated 112 million barrels of oil plus 3.8 billion cubic metres of gas

Wells 10 horizontal production wells, one gas injection well, plus one lower Cretaceous appraisal well planned. Three of the producing wells predrilled through preinstalled template, and existing appraisal well tied back to the platform.

Development partners

BP Exploration (operator)	62.75%
LASMO	16.21%
Mitsubishi Oil Company Exploration	11.18%
Clyde Petroleum	6.66%
Talisman Energy	3.20%

Platform facilities

Jacket

Four-legged steel tower weighing 6100t

Dimensions Height 134m; base 45m x 40m; top 28m x 24m

Piles 12 vertical skirt piles each 120m long by 2.43m diameter; weight 500t each; design penetration depth 100m

Conductors Eighteen 26in diameter, plus six 20in diameter tie-backs

Risers 10in oil and 8in gas export; 10in Cyrus oil import; 4in Cyrus gas lift; 2in methanol; 2in riser gas lift

Caissons One 42in diameter caisson containing risers and J-tube; nine other caissons

Template Preinstalled with six well slots; weight 138t

Integrated deck

Design capacities 58,000bpd oil and 1.16 million m³/d gas from Andrew; 12,000bpd oil from Cyrus Water handling 130,000bpd Gas export maximum rate of 1.13 million m³/d

Dimensions 75m long x 36m wide

Weights (including drilling and accommodation) 9620t dry; 10274t lift; 14880t design operating

Drilling facilities 1800t; 24 well slots

Accommodation module 72 beds; weight 520t

Flare tower 90m high; weight 130t

Processing Single train, two stage separation with gas dehydration

Power generation 3 x 6MW gas turbine (dual fuel) generators plus one 1MW emergency diesel generator

Gas compression HP and LP gas turbine export compressors; gas reinjection by electric drive compressor

Main pumps 2 x 100% electric drive seawater lift; 2 x 100% diesel drive firewater; 2 x 50% electric drive oil export

Air compression 2 x 50% electric drive compressors

Lifeboats 2 davit launched lifeboats each with capacity for full platform personnel complement

Cyrus field and subsea facilities

Location UK Block 16/28 7-10km north north east of Andrew

Discovery August 1979. In production from April 1990 to March 1992 through oil production vessel *Seillean*

Water depth 110m

Reservoir Palaeocene sandstone oil accumulation lying approximately 2500m below seabed

Recoverable reserves Estimated at 23.5 million barrels of oil

Wells 2 subsea wells tied back to Andrew platform

Licence operator BP Exploration 100%

Pipeline bundle 6.6km long. Towheads incorporating manifold at wells and subsea isolation valves for export pipelines. 28in diameter carrier pipe containing 10in oil production, 4in gas lift, 2in methanol pipelines, plus electrical cables and hydraulic tubing.

Oil export pipeline

16.2km long 10in diameter pipeline laid to existing valve tee No. 3 on Brae-Forties oil pipeline, with 45t seabed valve protection structure **Design pressure** 200 bar **Design input temperature** 105°C Pipeline trenched and buried. Oil delivered to Cruden Bay terminal.

Gas export pipeline

44km long, 8in diameter pipeline laid to existing valve tee No. 1 on CATS gas pipeline, with 91t seabed valve protection structure **Design pressure** 210 bar **Design input temperature** 75°C Pipeline trenched only. Gas delivered to Teesside terminal.

Andrew facilities alliance

BP Exploration
Andrew field operator

Brown & Root
Design, procurement and
management support

Trafalgar John Brown Oil and Gas
Integrated deck fabrication

BARMAC

Barmac
Jacket, template and piles fabrication

Saipem
Platform transportation and installation

Allseas
Oil and gas export pipelines procurement
and installation

Santa Fe
Drilling facilities design, procurement
and fabrication

Emtunga
Accomodation module design, procurement
and fabrication

Andrew development partners

BP Exploration

LASMO

MOC Exploration

Clyde Petroleum

Talisman Energy

Well engineering and operations alliances

Andrew template wells
BP Exploration
Baker Hughes Inteq
Santa Fe
Schlumberger IPM
Transocean

Cyrus subsea wells
BP Exploration
Baker Hughes Inteq
Schlumberger IPM
Transocean

Andrew and Cyrus operations
BP Exploration
Aramark
Asco
Baker Hughes Inteq
Brown & Root
Santa Fe
Schlumberger IPM

Cyrus alliance members

BP Exploration
Cyrus field operator

Rockwater
Cyrus bundle design
and installation

No business as usual

Facilities development schedule

Workscope	1994	1995
Jacket	Project sanction 4th February 1994	
Design		
Fabrication		
Integrated deck		
Design		
Fabrication		
Drilling module		
Design		
Fabrication		
Accommodation module		
Design		
Fabrication		
Pipelines & subsea structures		
Design		
Installation		
Template		
Design		
Drilling		
Offshore installation		
Template		
Platform		
Pipeline tie–ins		
Cyrus bundle & towheads		
Design		
Fabrication		
Installation		

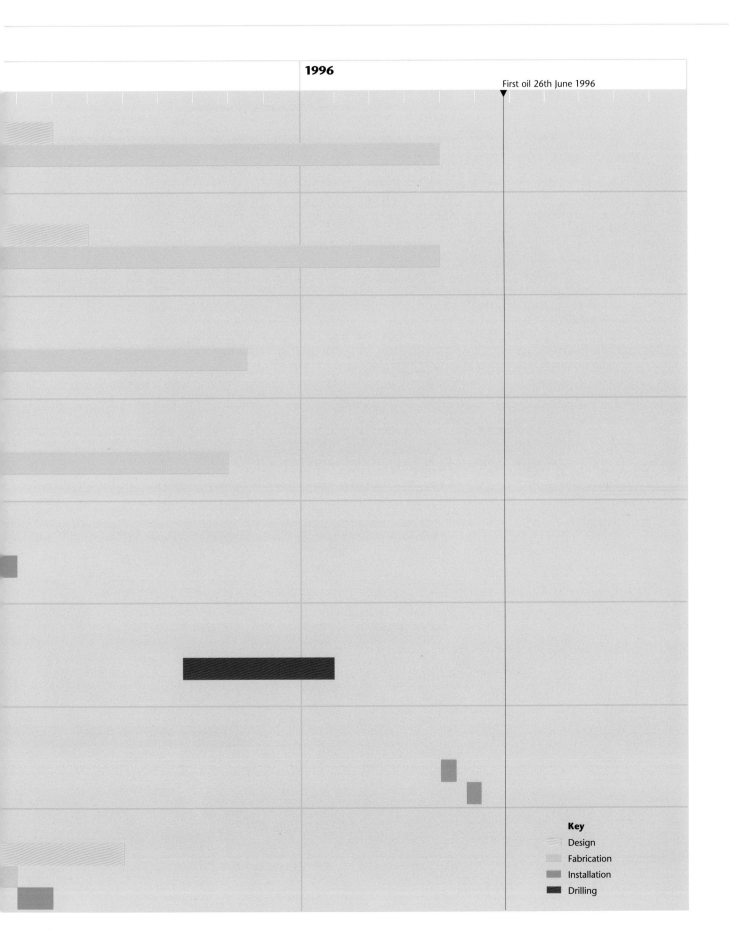

1996

First oil 26th June 1996

Key

Design
Fabrication
Installation
Drilling

No business as usual

Jacket

Subcontractors

British Pipe Coaters
Coatings of risers and guides

Det Norske Veritas
Jacket weighing

Mammoet Transport
Loadout of jacket

Norson Power
Flushing and testing of hydraulics

Pat Munro
Site civil works

Redpath Engineering Services
Forming of cones

Woodside Engineering
Fabrication of secondary steelwork

Suppliers

Avon Technology
Riser caisson seal

British Steel
Steel plate

CRP Marine
Riser caisson spacers

Hydrasun
Grout hoses and hydraulic fittings

K&B Beattie
Hydraulic hoses, hosebundle and winch

LFF
Pipe flanges and fittings

Morrison & Macdonald
Cold bending grout pipe, grout manifolds
and J-Tube bends

Murray International Metals
Steel plate

Oil States Rubber
Grout packers and wipers

Semark
Subsea markers

Sonsub
Subsea connectors

Varin Controls
Flood valves and actuators

Wilson Walton
Anodes

WJ Leigh
Paint

Integrated Deck

Subcontractors

Allerton Engineering
Secondary steel fabrication

AMEC Fabricators
Tubular rolling

Atlantic Engineering
Secondary steel fabrication

Baldwins Industrial Services
Major lifts and deck stacking

BARMAC
Tubular rolling

Barrier Offshore Engineering
Painting and passive fire protection

Cementation
Site civil works

Comtec
Nitrogen testing

Decima
Handrail fabrication

Far East Levingston Shipbuilding
Drilling facilities

G+H McGill
HVAC and architectural installation

Grayson, White and Sparrow
Deck stacking

Hartlepool Steel Fabrications
Secondary steel fabrication

Headley Purvis
Bolt tensioning

John Gibson Lifting Agencies
Weighing

Mammoet Transport
Loadout

Metfab
Pipe support fabrication

Nu–Town Fabrications
Pipe support fabrication

Redman Fisher Engineering
Open grid flooring

Redpath Engineering Services
Tubular rolling, pipe fabrication,
electrical and instrumentation installation

Rotary Services
HVAC fabrication

Smit International
Accommodation module installation

Suppliers

ABB Kent Introl
Choke and control valves

ABB Stal
Gas compressor driver

Able Instruments & Controls
Flowmeters

Airoil-Flaregas
Flare tips

Aqua Clear
Autochlorination

Avesta Stainless
Fittings and flanges, duplex and stainless steel pipe

Ayles Fermie International
Flaretip handling

Baker Hughes Process Systems
Seawater filter

Barton Firtop Eng
Flame arrestors and strainers

BD Profiles
Spectacle blinds, spades and drip rings

Bestobell Aviation
Fire seals

BICC
Electrical and instrument cable

Booth Industries
Firewalls, windows and doors

Bran & Luebbe
Methanol injection pumps

Brisco Engineering
Wellhead control system

British Steel
Structural steel plate

Bush Beach Engineering
Temperature transmitters and thermowells

Caproco International
Access fittings

Capital Valves Project Supply
Gate, globe and check valves

CP Hobal
Scrubbers, fuel gas knockout drum and degasser

Crosby Valve & Engineering
Relief valves

Danacoustic Marine Ceilings
Suspended ceilings

Daniel Industries
Oil and gas metering system

EAE
Offshore network telecommunications systems

E F Dowson
Cement sampler

Elequip
Electrical distribution system

ESL Fluid Handling
Helicopter refuelling, helideck roller guide

European Gas Turbines
Main power generation

Eurotube
Carbon steel fittings and flanges

Fischer & Porter
Variable area meter

Flangefitt Stainless
Carbon steel and stainless steel/duplex
fittings and flanges

Flexitallic
Gaskets

Fluorocarbon Company
PTFE sliding pads

Foxboro
Pneumatic controllers

Goodwin International
Dual plate check valves

Grove Italia
ESD, blowdown and manual ball valves

Halfen-Unistrut
Flooring

Halo Company
Platform identification signs

Handrail Design
Handrails and balustrading

Hans Leffer
Shell and tube heat exchangers

Heatex
Hot water calorifier, HP fuel gas superheater

Heatric
Compact heat exchanger

Hi-Lite Signs
Safety and information signs

Honeywell Control Systems
HVAC control system

Howard Butler
Receiver milliammeters

Howden Buffalo
HVAC fans

Hydrasun
Stainless steel and cupronickel pipe

IMAC
Partitions and doors

IMI Marston
Rupture disks

IMI Yorkshire Alloys
Cupronickel fittings and flanges

Ingersoll-Rand
Air compressor/dryer

ISA Controls
Orifice plates

James Walker
Gaskets

Jon Sivert Nielsen
Furniture and fixtures

K&B Beattie
Hoses and couplings

KDG Mobrey
Pressure transmitters

Knowsley SK
Deluge/sprinkler/foam skids,
fixed and portable fire monitors,
helideck and aviation fuel foam skids

Kvaerner FSSL
Control, monitoring and safety system; subsea control system

Lokomo
Jacket structural steel castings

London Fittings & Flanges
Carbon steel fittings and flanges

Magnetrol International
Level transmitters

Mannesmann Demag
Non-slam check valves

Mardale Pipes Plus
Stainless steel/duplex pipe fittings and flanges

Mech-Tool Engineering
Blastwalls

Merlin Fire & Security
Air sampling smoke detection tubing

Multi-Fluid International
Water in oil analysers

Motherwell Bridge
Separator fabrication

Murray International Metals
Structural steel sections and tubulars

Natco
Gas dehydration system

Oleochem
Laboratory equipment

Oliver Valves
Injection and sampling valves

Orga
Navigation aids

Paladon
Separator design

Panametrics
Moisture analysers

Parker Hannifin
Instrument fittings, valves, manifolds and monoblocs

Payne & Stames
Workshop equipment

PCT Group
Hoists and mechanical handling

Peerless Europe
Utility filter

Petrovalves
Through-conduit slab gate valves

Pipe Supports
Pipe supports

Powdermet
Hipped flanges

Promat Engineering Services
Flanged fittings

Redpath Engineering
Vessels

R Goodwin International
Dual plate check valves

Rollstud
Studbolts

Ross Electrical
Electrical bulk material

Safety Showers
Safety showers

Schat Watercraft
Lifeboats and davits

Scomark Engineering
Piping manifolds

Serck Baker
Hydrocyclones

Simco Engineers
Level gauges

Smith Flow Control
Interlocks

Solent & Pratt
Actuated and manual butterfly valves

Sound Attenuators
HVAC attenuators

Stothert & Pitt
Pedestal crane

Sulzer
Gas compressors

Techlok
Clamp type connectors

Tectubi SRL
Barred tees

Haigh Engineering
Sewage macerator

Thermon
Trace heating

TK Valve
Subsea ball valves

Tom Wheatley Valve Company
Valves

Transchem
Gate, globe and check valves

Tube Developments
Carbon steel pipe

Tube Sales & Services
Line pipe

Unitor
Nitrogen generator

Vanpipe
Chemical injection

Vomal International
Carbon steel fittings and flanges

Waterloo-Ozonair
HVAC equipment

Wefco
Separator fabrication

Weir Material Services
Duplex pipe

Weir Pumps
Main pumps

Wika Instruments
Temperature and pressure instruments

Wilson Supply International
Stainless steel/duplex fittings and flanges

Wood Group Fire Protection
Life saving appliances

Wormald Ansul
Fire hydrants, hoses and nozzles

Pipelines

Suppliers

BPCL
Polypropylene coating

Britannia
Anodes

Deltaflex
Gaskets

Dylan Steel
Flanges

Eres
Fittings

Promat
Nip-o-flanges

Raychem
Heat shrink sleeves

Rollstud
Nuts and bolts

SLP
Mattresses

Steels
Bends

Thyssen
Welding electrodes

TSSL
Linepipe

v Leeuwen
24in linepipe

Wilson Walton
24in anodes

Cyrus

Suppliers

ABB Control
Cable

Aberdeen Valve & Fitting
Stainless steel union elbows

Anderson Hydraulics
Stauff clamps

Balmoral Glass Fibre
Tube support units

BEL Valves
Gate valves

Blairchem
Inhibitor sticks

BPCL
Half shells

Buttings
Clad linepipe and bends

Duco
Umbilicals

Forth Tool & Gauge
Bulkheads

Halliburton
Grout connectors

Handy Harman
Stainless steel tubing

Highlander Fabrication
Actuator assemblies and diffusers

HS Pipe
Flood and vent valves

Isleburn
Chain

JGC Welding
Intermediate supports and pipeline spacers

John Lawrie
Chain

Kenmac
Double block and bleed valves

Lloyds Beal
Chain

MCT Brattberg
Lycab seal assemblies

Metrotec
Sealant and solvent

Nicholson Engineering
Transponder brackets and slip over sleeves

Ross Electrical
Cable ties

Sandem Slings
Ballast chain straps

Sigma North Sea
Control line clamps

TK Valve
Ball valves

TSSL
Carrier pipe

Whittaker Engineering
Fabrication valve mountings

Wilson Walton
Carrier anodes

About the author

Terry Knott is a distinguished oil industry journalist and chartered engineer with first-hand working experience of the international oil and gas business. Assignments for major oil companies, leading contractors and other organisations, in combination with regular contributions to journals and corporate publications, keep him in close contact with industry developments. He is widely travelled and has conducted information research in many of the established and emerging oil producing regions of the world.

In 1994 he was awarded the prestigious Offshore Northern Seas Press Prize for insightful editorial coverage of the industry's new strategies and technology, and in the following year was acknowledged by the Department of Trade and Industry in the United Kingdom and British Business Press for his reporting of innovation. His writing also helped British Petroleum to secure the new DTI 'Innovation in Industry' award in 1995.